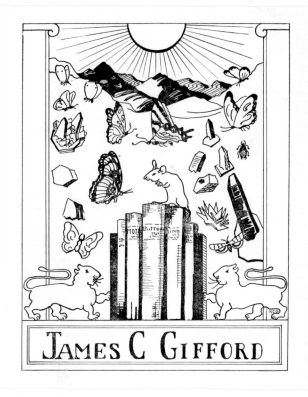

JAMES C GIFFORD

The Intelligence of Louis Agassiz

The Intelligence of

LOUIS AGASSIZ

A Specimen Book of

Scientific Writings

Selected, with an introduction and notes,

by GUY DAVENPORT

Foreword by Alfred S. Romer

Beacon Press   Boston

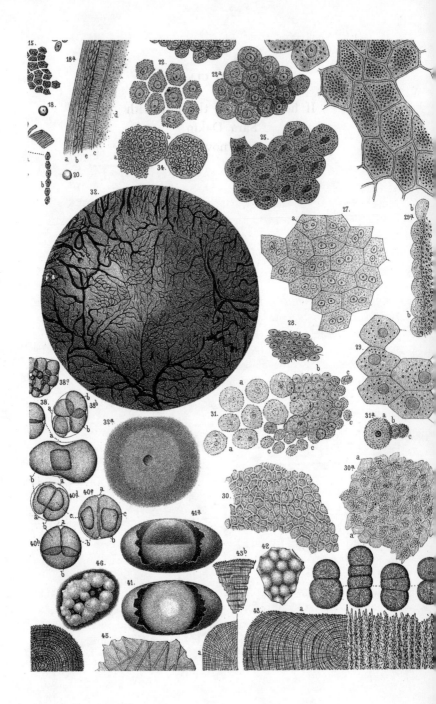

Foreword

The life of Louis Agassiz can be divided into two discrete chapters, each of brilliant achievement but of achievement in very different fields. Up to the time of his coming to America, at the age of forty, his life was that of a very distinguished research scientist. His accomplishments by the time he had finished his university career were already such as to make him the protégé of Cuvier and Humboldt, the two greatest naturalists of the time. Accepting a post in Neuchâtel in his native Switzerland, he singlehandedly turned this modest city into one of the major centers of research in Europe. During his fifteen years there he published, for example, more than two hundred research works, twenty of them substantial volumes illustrated with some two thousand plates. Among his most notable contributions were his survey of fossil fishes (his five volumes on the subject remain the basic work in this area of paleontology) and his advocacy of the theory of a widespread Pleistocene Ice Age, which now is universally accepted but at the time was vigorously opposed by almost every leading geologist.

The last quarter-century of his life, spent in America, was equally filled with accomplishment, but was very different in nature. Research retreated into the background. He began, it is true, a comprehensive series of "Contributions to the Natural History of the United States," but never progressed far with this, and the scientific work of his later years does not measure up, in either quantity or quality, to that of his European period.

"Louis Agassiz, teacher" was the way he described himself in his will. Correctly—for teaching was the outstanding feature of his American career. To scientists and educators it is his teaching of advanced students that is best remembered. At Harvard he gathered around him for instruction a series of young zoologists destined to become leaders in this field and who were, in turn, the teachers of later generations of American biologists. But more important in many ways was his influence on the general

American public. Through his lectures and writings he sought
to tell them something of the facts of natural history and of the
beauty and drama of the world of life. But, beyond this, his
teachings brought to thinking Americans the realization that science should form an integral and respected part of the country's
intellectual life.

Some years ago an old gentleman of my acquaintance told
me of a well-remembered day of his Philadelphia childhood, in
December 1873. Gloom descended upon the household with the
arrival of the morning paper. It continued as he walked abroad
with his father, who conversed with his friends in subdued and
solemn tones. To this small boy it seemed as if some major
calamity had occurred. In a sense it had, for the news had arrived
that the great Louis Agassiz was dead. To him—and perhaps to
his elders as well—it was almost as if science itself lay dead. For
to the people of that day Louis Agassiz was not just a scientist;
he was science embodied.

We can never meet Agassiz in the flesh, never feel the impact of the magnetic personality of which all speak who wrote
of him. William James gives part of the picture: "He was of so
commanding a presence, so curious and inquiring, so responsive
and expressive, and so generous of himself and of his own, that
everyone said of him: 'Here is no musty savant, but a man, a
great man.'" Nor can we ever hear the voice that captivated
his audiences; a voice which, his hearers tell us, was all the more
charming because of the persisting touch of accent and the occasional hesitation while he grasped for just the right word in his
adopted tongue.

But we do have his words. And they are indeed golden.
Most scientists are (it must be admitted) very poor writers. Some
express themselves so muddily that even workers in their own
fields have difficulty in understanding them. Others, a stage above
this, can convey their meaning, but often convey it haltingly.
Few have the ability which Agassiz possessed to write of science
not merely with clarity but with beauty. For the most part the
facts and theories which Agassiz presented are no longer in the
forefront of biological thought. But it is well that at least a selection of his writings be rescued from the semi-oblivion of the

back stacks of the library and be brought before the eyes of a modern audience as an example of what scientific writing ought to be—but usually is not.

The selections contained in this volume are excellent. Particularly of interest from the point of view of the history of scientific thought are the first and last. The "Essay on Classification" was written in 1857, when Agassiz was fifty years of age, fully matured in his mental development, and with a breadth in his background of study and research in natural science which few have ever equaled. In the hands of many men a work with such a title would have been a dry discussion of technical criteria for the erection of genera, families and other items in the "systematic" treatment of animals and plants. Agassiz's essay goes far beyond this. It is an exposition of his scientific philosophy as a whole. His concepts reflect to some degree his contacts with the idealism and *Naturphilosophie* of the days of his youth, tempered however by the emphasis on factual data preached by Cuvier. Our attempts at classifying animals, says Agassiz, are not attempts to institute order where none exists, but are, if intelligently done, a striving toward an understanding of an order in the universe which is already there, established by the Creator. He believes that it can be demonstrated, and demonstrated to his satisfaction in this essay, "that man has not invented but only traced, this systematic arrangement in nature; . . . that this plan of creation, which so commends itself to our highest wisdom . . . was the free conception of the Almighty Intellect, matured in his thought before it was manifested in tangible external forms." All species of animals were created separately, in accordance with a foreordained pattern, in the form in which we find them, and are destined to remain unchanged.

An orderly concept, beautifully expressed, in which science and religion are at peace in a happy universe. The alternative, to Agassiz? "The desolate theory which refers us to the laws of matter as accounting for all the wonders of the universe, and leaves us with no God but the monotonous, unvarying action of physical forces, binding all things to their inevitable destiny."

The "Essay" was published in 1857. The next year Darwin and Wallace's preliminary papers on evolution were published;

The Origin of Species appeared in 1859. Darwin was a much poorer writer than Agassiz; but, like Agassiz, he marshaled facts in support of his theories, and marshaled them so effectively that, year by year, those who had once believed the Agassiz picture, were converted to evolutionary beliefs. But for Agassiz the situation was an impossible one. Belief in separate creation was essential in his philosophy of nature. To abandon this would bring destruction to his basic concepts—and destruction to Agassiz himself. And so, for the next fifteen years, we see him fighting a losing battle, denying time after time the reality of evolution. One cannot but have a feeling of sympathy and sadness for a lost cause on reading the final selection, "Evolution and Permanence of Type," written in Agassiz's last days and published after his death—an essay valiantly and beautifully written, but carrying conviction to few of his scientific readers then and none now. Today scientists are, like Agassiz, seeking to discern an order in nature, believing that order must be there, but groping toward it without Agassiz's faith that divine wisdom lies behind it. Among the cares and troubles of adult life, one often wishes he were able to escape back to childhood and the warm safety of his mother's arms. Just so, I think, do many scientists wish, vainly, that they could escape from the doubts and confusions of the universe we dimly see about us and return to the peace and serenity of that order of nature which Agassiz so eloquently expounded.

ALFRED S. ROMER

Director Emeritus, Museum of Comparative Zoology,
Harvard University

Contents

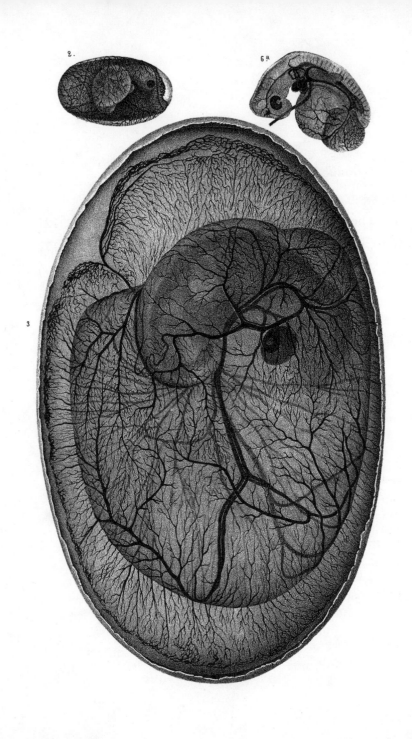

Introduction

I. BEYOND THE GLASS FLOWERS

Brown Séquard tells me I must not think. Nobody can ever know the tortures I endure in trying to stop thinking.

LOUIS AGASSIZ, just before dying of fatigue

This is a man who, at the height of Napoleon's power, refused the directorship of the Garden of Plants, and a seat as senator of the empire. He might, with little pains, have been rich; but he is penniless, after much toil, and the very house over his head is mortgaged to support a museum which belongs to other people.

THEODORE LYMAN, *Recollections of Agassiz*

In the 1904 Baedeker for the United States, the English tourist in Cambridge, Massachusetts, had recommended to him "the University Museum (Director, Prof. Alexander Agassiz), containing valuable collections of comparative zoology," the starred attraction being "the glass flowers at Harvard" which, Marianne Moore's father observed, superior people never make long trips to see. Mr. Moore was at least half satiric in his observation, but his intuition was perfect in suspecting that the glass flowers were ridiculous. They are, in fact, a symbol of Agassiz's achievement as it survives. His great museum of natural history is an appendage to Victorian simulacra; his reputation is thought to be part of the American dullness in the late nineteenth century.

Among the contributors of specimens to Agassiz's great unfinished work on the natural history of the United States we find "Mr. D. Henry Thoreau, of Concord," who is not to be wholly identified with the transcendental hermit of the literary handbooks, author of *Walden* and one lesser book. The Thoreau to whom Agassiz made his acknowledgment was a scientist, the pioneer ecologist, one of the few men in America with whom

1

he could talk, as on an occasion when the two went exhaustively into the mating of turtles, to the dismay of their host for dinner, Emerson.

"Several score of the best-educated, most agreeable, and personally the most sociable people in America united in Cambridge to make a social desert that would have starved a polar bear," Henry Adams says in the *Education*. "The liveliest and most agreeable of men—James Russell Lowell, Francis J. Child, Louis Agassiz, his son Alexander, Gurney, John Fiske, William James and a dozen others, who would have made the joy of London or Paris—tried their best to break out and be like other men in Cambridge and Boston, but society called them professors, and professors they had to be." One reason that Agassiz is the subject for many romantic biographies, many inspiring books for children, and a mysterious figure in American intellectual history is that he moved among people who paid him every compliment except comprehension. He lectured everywhere, brilliantly. His lectures took the highest reward of nineteenth-century fame: parody. Artemus Ward and Josh Billings gave splendid satires of them, assuring audiences who had sat through Agassiz's masterful zoologizing that the hen is a fool and the mule an oversight. These dedicated audiences enjoyed Agassiz and Artemus Ward with compartmentalized minds, never realizing the humor as a higher appreciation than their own desperate patronage.

Thoreau's finest thought remained in the privacy of his rich notebooks because of the dullness of the public interest, which he treated to inspired insults and ironic exhortations, daring to risk his meditations on its blank surface. Agassiz remained charmingly gracious to this same audience, vaguely aware that it was there. He would talk natural history with professor or stable boy; what mattered was that he could focus an idea out loud. Agassiz made a wild guess about the autumn leaf, calling its color a maturation. Dutifully all the poetlings and ladies' diaries took up the phrase, "the maturing of the leaf." Emerson displayed a conceit about the account of the Brazilian expedition, a collaboration between Agassiz and his wife, saying that the book was like a mermaid, so harmonious was the combination of ichthyology and travelogue. This promptly became a Boston riddle: "Why is the Agassiz Brazilian book like a mermaid?" "Because you can't tell where the lady begins and the fish leaves off."

Watch an English artist within this insipidity. Marianne North, the painter, visited the Cambridge of Agassiz just weeks before her incredible debut at the White House as the daughter of Lord North, Earl of Guilford (fl. 1776)—Ulysses Grant even inquired as to his lordship's health. She perceived a level of culture at the Adams', but then she began to meet people who wept over Dickens, and people who were trying the mermaid riddle one more time, and ladies who "wept bitterly" when Miss North sang after dinner, and the Miss Longfellows introduced themselves on the streetcar, and took her to lunch. "The luncheon was worthy of a poet—nothing but cakes and fruit, and cold tea with lumps of ice in it." Longfellow was "full of pleasant unpractical talk, quite too good for everyday use."

But in Agassiz, though she had been told that he was "the clever old Swiss professor" who had married "a most agreeable handsome woman" and a Bostonian to boot, she found a man "more to my mind," who "gave me a less poetical dinner." Darwin had been a little like this, full of Linnaean binomials for everything, a man who had looked and seen. Agassiz was more congenial, seeming "entirely content with himself and everyone else." His museum was a catalogue of nature. He called himself the librarian of the works of God, scarcely a facile image in its implications.

For all her advantage as an outsider, Marianne North perceived only that Agassiz was a man far above the intellectual atmosphere in which she found him. And he has remained a figure of unquestioned stature in American intellectual history. Few, however, can attach any reality to his vaguely familiar, vaguely exotic name. William James and Henry Adams would have thought this impossible, certainly unlikely. But in neither F. O. Matthiesen's *American Renaissance* nor the comprehensive Spiller, Thorp, Canby and Johnson *Literary History of the United States* will one find Agassiz mentioned, much less related to the minds upon which he pressed such influence. The obscurest subject in the curricula of American colleges is the intellectual history of the United States. Like American history itself, intellectual achievement has been stylized into an episode myth in which the mind has no real prominence. Patrick Henry has become a single sentence; John Randolph has disappeared. The American scholar who found in his eightieth year the vestige of mankind's first cultivation of cereals is as unknown to American history as the tactician who drove Cornwallis into Washington's hands.

This book, then, is in the nature of an exultation. The exultation is not over discovery, for Agassiz has had abundant attention, and interest in him is growing. The Agassiz legend is just that, legendary. Anecdotes live in scholastic folklore. Everyone agrees that Agassiz is a heritage. But what kind of heritage? Once one has discovered that beneath the legend is a system of ideas, it becomes apparent how wrong it is that Agassiz's writing has lain unpublished for over a century. This book is a gallery of exhibits from that writing, made in the faith that authenticities count, that Agassiz need not be held on trust as a mind which illuminated certain scientific matters in the nineteenth century and now must live in history as a reputation wholly fabulous.

II. VERBAL PRECISION

Philosophers and theologians have yet to learn that a physical fact is as sacred as a moral principle. Our own nature demands from us this double allegiance.

The Natural History of the United States

Now that at mid-century we have Louise Hall Tharp's *Adventurous Alliance: The Story of the Agassiz Family of Boston* (Little, Brown, 1959) and Edward Lurie's *Louis Agassiz: A Life in Science* (University of Chicago, 1960), the asperity is diminished in having to witness the survival of Agassiz's genius as a facile and homely myth except for the almost secret publication by John Kasper and Ezra Pound, of an abominably printed but wholly admirable collection of paragraphs entitled *Gists from*

Agassiz, or Passages on the Intelligence Working in Nature,
(Square Dollar Series, Washington, 1953). This inspired, ninety-
six-page pamphlet was both the fruit of Pound's homework for
the *Rock-Drill* cantos and Kasper's exploration, under Pound's
tutelage, of an American writer of greatest caliber now lost from
curricula, a neglected classic which, in the unflagging diligence
that turned up Alexander Del Mar, Senator Thomas Hart
Benton, John Randolph of Roanoke, and like treasure, Pound
recovered for his pupils from his dismal quarters in those four-
teen Washington years. Hence the publishers found it expedient
to note that a classical education is not "the mere adjunct of an
art shop or a collection of antiques, but a preparation for contemporary life." The first three lines of the *Paradiso* made its
epigraph:

> La gloria di colui che tutto move
>   per l'universo penetra e risplende
>   in una parte più e meno altrove.

Behind that alignment of scientist and poet who were gazing
at the same intricate design of nature there is an equally fine,
invisible intelligence to be discerned, and without detracting
from John Kasper's diligence, rather congratulating him that his
teacher was pleased to collaborate anonymously, we can identify
the unmistakable voice of Ezra Pound on the book's jacket:

The boredom caused by "American culture" of the second half
of the XIXth century was due largely to its being offered as "something
like" English culture, but rather less lively; something to join Tennyson
in "The Abbey" perhaps, but nothing quite as exciting as Browning, or
Fitzgerald's *Rubaiyat*.

Agassiz, apart from his brilliant achievements in natural science,
ranks as a writer of prose, precise knowledge of his subject leading to
great exactitude of expression.

Agassiz, who as a freshman at Heidelberg knew more about
fish than he was able to find from his professors or in their
libraries, and whose last act in a life as creative as that of
Leonardo or Picasso, was to sail along the route of the *Beagle*
before announcing his final and authoritative rejection of evolu-

tion,[1] would as soon have laid down his Pliny and Aristotle as his Baer or Cuvier.

This introduction, then, can dispense with the Agassiz myth. The man is unprofitable to inspect, anyway. The beautiful genius of his wife's two-volume *Life and Letters* (1885), the charming, gallant professor and *nonpareil* of Mrs. Tharp's biography, and the tragic egotist of Edward Lurie's scientific record of a career which lasted into its own anguished obsolescence—one hesitates to accept any of these as Agassiz "the man," who will remain, whatever else we may do to his biography, the very spirit of inquiry and analysis.

Agassiz was a major figure in American nineteenth-century culture, as much a part of our literary history as our scientific. Agassiz assumed that the structure of the natural world was everyone's interest, that every community as a matter of course would collect and classify its zoology and botany. College students can now scarcely make their way through a poem organized around natural facts. Ignorance of natural history has become an aesthetic problem in reading the arts. Thoreau, though he wondered why the very dogs did not stop and admire turned maples, knew better what the American attitude was, and was to be, toward natural history. Nullity.

The place scientific writing might claim among the corpus of imaginative writing zoned off as literature by unstable rules for admission and rejection is a strong one, allowing for inevitable airs of condescension from the protectors of letters. The spirit of

[1] See Elizabeth Cary Agassiz, "In the Straits of Magellan," pp. 89-95, Vol. XXXI, 1873, *The Atlantic Monthly,* and her "Cruise through the Galapagos," pp. 579-584, *ibid.* This voyage of the *Hassler* was mainly oceanographic. Agassiz saw the opportunity "to study the whole Darwinian theory free from all external influences and former prejudices," as he wrote to a German friend, Carl Gegenbaur, adding that "It was on a similar voyage that Darwin himself came to formulate his theories!" Edward Lurie's account of this voyage, pp. 372-377 of his *Louis Agassiz: A Life in Science,* University of Chicago, 1960, is particularly fine. The crystallized rejection of Darwinian theory was published in 1874, "Evolution and Permanence of Type," pp. 92-101, *The Atlantic Monthly,* Vol. XXXIII. The student of iconography is invited to compare the Galapagos as they appeared to Darwin, Mrs. Agassiz, and Melville, whose sustained vastation in *Las Encantadas* is a prophetic view of the impact of evolutionary data on the imaginative mind.

our age has been curiously denying, although its search for purity is understandable. The American in particular regards his mind as a showroom for certain furnitures as content, and this silly idea gets defended by the vulgar error that if the mind is stuffed, there'll be no room for important things in their time. I first collided with this homely belief while teaching in St. Louis, that museum of Americana, and should have known that it came from Poor Richard or Sherlock Holmes. It is from Holmes. At a more crucial level our very schools and journals encourage neglecting everything but some approved matter at hand. Even in so fine a morphology of literary form as Northrop Frye's *Anatomy of Criticism*, the shape of scientific writing gets but a passing glance (a sharp one, however).

Agassiz's masterpiece was to have been the *Contributions to the Natural History of the United States*. Its four handsome volumes remain as a triumph of thought and scholarship. So carefully do they begin, holding entire libraries of fact in perfect balance with original research, that the mind wonders at the inconceivably fine book the finished work would have been; for in 1,600 pages Agassiz has but described the embryology of the North American turtles and the anatomy of the most elusive and perishable of creatures, the jellyfish and his kin. "Jellyfish?" a Transcendentalist once asked Agassiz. "It seems to be little more than organized water."

Because it is fairly easy, and always engrossing, to make Agassiz the man a captivating subject, I have focused on his achievement, and this book is primarily an anthology of his writing. Reading Agassiz, however, is an aesthetic pleasure in itself, so it is hoped that the book serves as much as a celebration of his genius as a small record of it.

"Agassiz's influence on methods of teaching," William James reported to the American Society of Naturalists in 1896, "was prompt and decisive,—all the more so that it struck people's imagination by its very excess. The good old way of committing printed abstractions to memory seems never to have received such a shock as it encountered at his hands." That shock is still potent, and the spirit of Agassiz, as we find it now in his writings, would be a welcome one in the American classroom.

The ability to combine facts, he said at the end of his life, is a much rarer gift than to discern them. This observation has weight. The man who said it had combined facts enough, and when he held fire on evolution he had, as Darwin knew, more facts than Darwin to combine, but he was also the man who discerned what a glacier was, and the evidence of the Ice Age, and who cancelled species after species identified by his colleagues by pointing out that the new-found creature was but the pup of a well-known animal.

It has been said too often, especially as a motive for shelving Agassiz as a romantic biologist, that he refused to see the truth of evolution because it wasn't his discovery. This is easy to believe, difficult to prove.

The accuracy of his eye is more important than five hundred anecdotes of Cambridge life, and anyway his role as upsetter of the Harvard ambience sounds like (and, one hopes, was) an unsuspected maliciousness of fumigatory intent rather than the amusing mishaps of a sweet, *distrait* scientist. The snakes that the Boston ladies found beside them on the settee in the Agassiz parlor, the lizards and toads produced at transcendental dinners (one must overlook these deep thinkers), and the drunken bear stalking what is now Massachusetts Avenue (one of Professor Agassiz's specimens), and a thousand other inadvertences, can scarcely all have been unplanned. The Harvard in which Agassiz halfheartedly submitted to the bit part of tame professor, the Harvard of Longfellow and James Russell Lowell, elicited gestures of self-defense. It was the Harvard which dynamited Raphael Pumpelly's bride (an error in victims, the charge being intended for a local tease), thereby alienating a brilliant mind. Agassiz found the Cambridge High School's chemistry lab better than Harvard's and worked there; his major biological work he did for a while in an abandoned bath house on the Charles, and later in a wooden building which was twice moved to greater distances from the Yard. It was the Harvard which denied Thoreau the use of its library.

The writing here collected from the work of Louis Agassiz, teacher, is not representative of his range as a scientist nor is it able to watch him at his bedrock-mounted microscope tipping a watch-glass in which yellow granular cells in unfertilized turtle *ova* are like "glass globes whirling along, freighted on one side with golden pebbles." *To watch* is the verb; the verbal precision of Agassiz's prose, unmatched in American literature, can sustain for fifty pages a lucid description of the inside of an egg. When the "hyaline masses" of these *ova* are swollen with water to learn the tensile strength of the "glass globe," one five-hundredth of an inch in diameter, the yolk grains "dance about their confined sphere in a zigzag quiver, and finally their delicate boundary wall, which by this time has become unequivocally demonstrated, bursts suddenly on one side, and extrudes at a single contractive effort nearly the whole horde of its vivacious motes, assuming itself by this loss a wrinkled, unsymmetrical, much diminished shape, but still holding a few oscillating corpuscles."

The present collection of passages from Agassiz has been made not only for the reader who can be interested in the shouted-down side of an argument a hundred years old, but also as a celebration of verbal precision. Darwin's prose, beside Agassiz's, is wordy, undistinguished, indecisive as to its audience. Agassiz was both popular lecturer and essayist; we are not surprised to find his scientific prose elegantly exact, scrupulous in its details. It has the eloquence of information, but it also has a brilliance all its own which flashes from deep sensibility and sharp awareness of beauty.

In a long, formal essay on the embryology of the turtle, we find these sentences in a study of the eggshell:

The outermost of these layers, next to the hard calcareous deposit, are composed of the smoothest and most uniform fibres, resembling at times excessively elongated tubular crystals. Before the shell is deposited, these layers may be recognized by the peculiarly brilliant nacreous appearance which strikes the eye. In Glyptemys insculpta, where this has been noticed most frequently, the component fibres are of excessive tenuity and compactness among each other, the latter feature tending, no doubt, to heighten the polished aspect of the surface of the layer.

Agassiz wrote comfortably in French, German and Latin; English he learned late and was never at ease speaking it and rejoiced when, in Brazil or exploiting the pretensions of Cambridge society, he could lecture in French. His written English, like Conrad's, depended heavily on the easy cliché, hence "resembling at times," "may be recognized," "which strikes the eye," "the latter feature tending," and "aspect" in this passage, a judicious picking from that smooth Victorian literacy from which few native writers escaped, Ruskin alone, perhaps, toward the end of his life. A necessary verbal conciseness gives the passage "calcareous," "tubular crystals," "nacreous," "tenuity and compactness." It is Agassiz's clarity of mind that makes the sentence pleasant to read and allows it to be accessible to the reader who exults in precision as a quality of mind.

The earliest indication of a mesoblast is manifested by a slight haziness at one single point within the ectoblast, close against its wall.

When the Purkinjean vesicle has reached a size but a little larger than that of the last, the Wagnerian vesicles almost entirely cover the wall of their parent, simulating, by their clearness and roundness of contour, drops of dew lining a glass globe.

The clear, transparent nature of the younger states of the Wagnerian vesicles is gradually lost in a certain measure, and superseded by a pearly or milky complection bounded by a rather dark, soft outline, calling to mind the appearance of the denser species of Medusae, or the bluish transparency of boiled cartilage; at the same time there appears a very bright, irrefractive, eccentric spot, the Valentinian vesicle.

Not the artist but that fiction the public considers the scientist an alien. An approved and perhaps journalistically hatched topic of the day is the dichotomy of humanist and scientist, and atomic physicists are treated as if they were Martians, humanists as from Arcadia, while the journalists who pit one against the other apparently went to school to the angelic intelligences, happy to explain humanism to the scientist, science to the humanist. But look! Photography, as Bouvard or Bloom will tell you, was a blow to art, rivaling, demoralizing and displacing it.

Yet we cannot find the frightened artist or the sanguine photographer to give substance to this *idée reçue*. We can find Renoir ecstatic over photographic tone, Stieglitz sponsoring a whole movement in modern painting, a company of French painters staying up all night looking at Muybridge's photographs, and on and on, not to mention the distinguished list of painter-photographers. We should be especially suspicious of the advertised antagonism between students of matter in terms of natural law and students of all things in whatever terms. One of the most provocative books on the biology of sex is by a poet, Rémy de Gourmont; one of the finest on art, by a scientist, Leo Frobenius.[2] One could fill pages with the sensibility of da Vinci; a painter invented the electric telegraph; the great poem *Paterson* was written by a doctor.

The line of distinction is misdrawn. Redraw it to zone sensibility from barbarity, and such an intelligence as Agassiz's will need no apology. The fact that a misplaced distinction exists leads us into dissociating

RIBES BRACTEOSUM, Dougl. Unarmed, glabrous; leaves on long petioles, cordate, deeply 5-7 lobed, sprinkled with resinous dots beneath, the lobes acuminate, coarsely doubly serrate or incised; racemes long, erect, many-flowered, on short peduncles; calyx rotate, glabrous; flowers white; fruit black, resinous-dotted and scarcely eatable.

from this definition of love by a poet:

> Where memory liveth,
>   it takes its state
> Formed like a diafan from light on shade
>
> Which shadow cometh of Mars and remaineth
> Created, having a name sensate,
> Custom of the soul,
>   will from the heart;
>
> Cometh from a seen form which being understood
> Taketh locus and remaining in the intellect possible

[2] I mean Gourmont's *Physique de l'amour: essai sur l'instinct sexuel* (1904) and Frobenius' *Erlebte Erdteile*, especially Vol. IV: *Paideuma* (1928, Frankfurt).

Wherein hath he neither weight nor still-standing
Descendeth not by quality but shineth out
Himself his own effect unendingly
Not in delight but in the being aware
Nor can he leave his true likeness otherwhere.

The first, from Sereno Watson's *Botany* (*United States Geological Exploration of the Fortieth Parallel,* 1871) is as severely disciplined a record of a prairie gooseberry as Guido Cavalcanti's poem is a closely argued, scholastic definition of love's attributes. So confused is the present delinquency from verbal precision that many sophomores and many professors will unhesitatingly declare this paragraph a hopeless specimen of pedantry, "scientific jargon." It is unimaginable that these professors and sophomores cannot appreciate the diction which named a jellyfish *Medusa* or chose as Linnaean binomials for Wyoming flora *Artemisia frigida, Helenium autumnale, Fritillaria pudica, Helianthus exilis* and *Gilia ciliata.* Samuel Johnson is palmed off in classrooms as a harmless drudge of a lexicographer, yet open the *Dictionary* anywhere and find precision and eloquent plainness. "POKER: *The iron bar with which men stir the fire.* POETESS: *A she poet.* HORSE: *A neighing quadruped, used in war and draught and carriage.*" Watson's description of the gooseberry is within a tradition of exactitude which was never divorced from sensibility. Scientific language (which, like poetry, is cared for word by word) is as interesting to the artist as the language of fine prose and poetry to the scientist. Botanical nomenclature, for instance, is transparent, unbetrayed into the opacity of use by rote. *Viola saint-pauliana,* the African violet, was discovered and named by a Christian missionary. This is not a fact; cultures can be deduced from any fragment thereof.[3] *Helenium autumnale* bears its original Greek name, aligning flower and woman in the deep tradition that awed and pleased John Ruskin, and a nineteenth-

---

[3] *Nequiquam, quoniam medio de fonte leporum surgit amari aliquit quod in ipsis floribus angat!* "I hate to disillusion you," Agassiz's successor writes with Agassizian kindness, "but the name was given by a professional botanist in Hannover, Wendland, who, as far as I know, never went abroad; the name is in honor of a German nobleman, Baron Walter von Saint Paul, who brought a specimen back from Africa."

century botanist added *autumnale,* specifying both its flowering
season and the botanist's world-weary nostalgia over classical
culture, so that one cannot distinguish between the poetry and
the science of the name; they are fused—a name fitted with
precision into a universal nomenclature for all the *flora* and an
image of a tall, aging heroine. The common name for *Helenium
autumnale* is sneezeweed, and one perceives a known culture in
that, too.

The second passage is a translation (by Ezra Pound, in
Canto XXXVI) of a medieval poem which defines love. It does
not define with terms any less clear than those of a psychologist,
and if we are willing we can easily see the scientific precision
of the poet with the same eyes that detect the poetic precision
of the botanist. To see Sereno Watson and a medieval poet
within one frame is not only an advantage and privilege to the
perceptor; it is also an invitation to read with new eyes. The
index to culture is sensitivity. Our culture can be gauged as
exultantly in Agassiz's long study of the naked-eyed Medusa as
in Marianne Moore's dilation upon the edge-hog. But where can
we find the teachers to talk about the two in one context? Even
Wallace Stevens, in a brilliant and congenial essay in *The Necessary Angel,* compared Miss Moore's ostrich not with an ostrich
but with the article on ostriches in the *Britannica,* that *pons
asinorum.*

In Lowell's stultifying elegy, *Agassiz,* we find:

> . . . in him perhaps
> Science had barred the gate that lets in dream,
> And he would rather count the perch and bream.

Lowell allows Agassiz "the poet's open eye," but metaphori-
cally only, for he suspected that so great a grasp of nature must
coincide somewhere with the Wordsworthian sensibilities he
dealt in. It is fairly clear that Lowell had no way of conceiving
of Agassiz and Wordsworth as writers within the same range of
meditation. Lowell himself was two men, the one not on speaking
terms with the other. His comic alter ego Bigelow had a viable
diction and wit. The official poet called "James Russell Lowell"

could only manipulate, with a variety of ineptitudes, a collection of verbal tags and imitated emotions from Wordsworth, Milton and Gray. The elegy to Agassiz's memory, written in Florence and dispatched to *The Atlantic Monthly,* is almost a good poem. He cannot hide Agassiz with his pomposity. He knew the man too well, and good phrases get in despite the poem's commitment to a high diction. We accept as accurate "his broad maturity" (Lowell perceiving a mind that had actually arrived at ideas and was not merely hankering for them). We can see Agassiz in "his wise forefinger raised in smiling blame," and in similar clear passages. But we read the poem with bleak appreciation, though we learn from Lowell's every gesture why the real excellence of Louis Agassiz is unknown to American students, and why American intellectual life (that "level monotone," as Lowell called it) could make nothing at all of the genius who came to live and work in it.

III. INTELLIGENCES

Agassiz tells his class that the intestinal worms in the mouse are not developed except in the stomach of the cat.

Picked up, floating, an *Emys picta,* hatched last year. It is an inch and one-twentieth long in the upper shell and agrees with Agassiz's description at that age. Agassiz says he could never obtain a specimen of the *insculpta* only one year old, it is so rarely met with, and young *Emydidae* are so aquatic. I have seen them frequently.

Agassiz says he has discovered that the haddock, a *deep-sea fish,* is viviparous.

March 20. Dine with Agassiz at R. W. E.'s. He thinks that the suckers die of asphyxia, having very large air-bladders and being in the habit of coming to the surface for air. But then he is thinking of a different phenomenon from the one I speak of, which last is confined to the very earliest spring or winter. He says that the *Emys picta* does not copulate till seven years old, and then does not lay till four years after copulation, or when eleven years old. The *Cistudo Blandingii* (which he has heard of in Massachusetts only at Lancaster) copulates at eight or nine years of age. He says this is not a *Cistudo* but an *Emys*. He has eggs of the *serpentina* from which the young did not come forth till the next spring. He thinks that the Esquimau dog is the only indigenous one in the United States. He had not observed the silvery appearance and dryness of the lycoperdon fungus in water which I showed. He had broken caterpillars and found the crystals of ice in them, but had not thawed them. When I began to tell him of my experiment on a frozen fish, he said that Pallas had shown that fishes were frozen and thawed again, but I affirmed the contrary, and then Agassiz agreed with me. Says Aristotle describes the care the pouts take of their young. I told him of Tanner's account of it, the only one I had seen.

The river over the meadows again, nearly as high as in February, on account of the rain of the 19th.

Thoreau, The Journals

From the Lakedaimonian cabin at Walden Pond, Thoreau sent to Agassiz fish, snapping turtles, snakes, whatever he thought the professor might not know. Throughout the *Journals,* and even in *Walden* and the *Week on the Concord and Merrimac Rivers,* we find Thoreau exulting to have found things as yet unclassified. Agassiz paid well and Thoreau needed the money. When funds were low, Thoreau would advertise the riches of Walden to Agassiz's assistant, the naturalist Elliot Cabot: minks, muskrats, frogs, lizards, tortoises, snakes, caddie-worms, leeches, muscles, "etc., or rather, *here they are.*" For the great *Natural History of the United States,* Thoreau on one occasion made up an impressive shipment of his elected neighbors. From the pond came fifteen pouts, seventeen perch, thirteen shiners, one land and five mud tortoises. From the river came seven perch, five shiners, eight bream, four dace, two mud and five painted tortoises. The cabin itself gave up a black snake and a dormouse.

Agassiz, forever lecturing, forever searching out money for his collections—"I am too busy to make a living"—regarded Thoreau's detachment from the world with envy. "My only business is my intercourse with nature," he wrote to Thoreau in 1849, "and could I do without draughtsmen, lithographers, etc.,

I would live still more retired. This will satisfy you that whenever you come this way I shall be delighted to see you—since I have also heard something of your mode of living."

No one sent in such fresh fish as Thoreau, or seemed to know so intuitively what would please Agassiz, who, soon aware that his collector was no mean naturalist, began to cast his orders as hints ("I do not know how much trouble I may be giving Mr. Thoreau"). And his letters to Thoreau began to take on professional tones: ". . . the small mud turtle was really the *Sternothoerus odoratus,* as I suspected,—a very rare species, quite distinct from the snapping turtle." More than once Agassiz came to the cabin at Walden "to look after new *Leucisci,*" and to inspect turtles.

Looking at these two a hundred and twenty-odd years away, we perceive a curious touching of worlds. It is not, even now, known who Thoreau was, what science, purposefully unseparated from meditation, lies in the notebooks and journals. One distillation from his extraordinary reading of nature is *Walden;* given other precipitates, we can coagulate other systems of stuff. He was clearly an ecologist; he was also a student of time, of cyclic movements in nature and of the miraculously synchronous organization of plants and animals. Hence his daily inspection of one woodscape, knowing every detail of its life. Agassiz knew oceans, continents, mountains; he had lived on a glacier as Thoreau lived at Walden. But Thoreau did not know Agassiz any more than Agassiz knew Thoreau. These two minds of intense brightness were equally familiar with the shyness of turtles; each knew the unsuspected mysteries of nature, seeing more than they would ever have time to record.

But notice, however remote these conversations of Agassiz and Thoreau must remain to us, that' the two figures—portly, bald Agassiz, shaggy, nimble Thoreau—bent over a painted turtle at Walden, change a great deal of our attitude as to what the nineteenth century called Nature. Bryant, Whittier, Emerson; Lowell, Longfellow, Holmes—they knew their Romanticism; they knew how to arrive at the "Wordsworthian impulses." Yet they could also focus on leaf or meadow with something of the discipline of a Japanese poet (and spoil their gaze, to be sure, with an easy moralizing). Their work is now considered dull. Go back to it, however. Be patient or kindly blind to their interpretive gestures. Look with their eyes at the physical world that held their attention: it is the symbol of the age's profound attachment to biological fact. Not rusticity merely or picnic-day ebullience, their engagement was aesthetic, faithful, an intuition of ultimate authenticities. Thoreau's love affair with the scrub-oak, homeliest of trees, began to have the qualities of myth, the Greek feeling for the olive which we find in *Oedipus at Colonus*.

IV. METAMORPHOSIS: AGASSIZ AND DARWIN

Hindsight instructs us to wonder why Agassiz could not see the truth of Evolution. But hindsight also reminds us that Agassiz consistently located intelligence *in* or *behind* nature, long before Bergson, Whitehead and Wittgenstein were forced by logic to return intelligence to nature, as man had assumed from the beginning of thought, rather than live with the miserable confusions of nineteenth-century mechanism. Darwin's superimposition of Progress upon the processes of Evolution taxes pure empiricism more than Agassiz's finding an intelligent plan or even a divinity in nature. If Darwin's mechanism of natural selection has the merit of doing away with a single act of creation, it nevertheless leads to the embarrassment of introducing both purpose in nature and cognition in the evolutionist as *dei ex machina*. This difficulty has sufficiently impressed some of the acutest twentieth-century scientists and philosophers of science to lead them into doctrines of multiple acts of creation and even into attributing spontaneity, awareness and purpose to all natural processes. But in order not to distort, from our privileged point in time, a "vanquished viewpoint," let us simply note that Agassiz's writings in natural history and systematic biology are equally imperative reading for us, and let us consider whether a passage such as the following, from Agassiz's "Essay on Classification," is a last and most explicit statement of pre-Darwinian teleology or whether it is a suggestive precursor of post-Darwinian teleology and natural philosophy:

But, which is the truly humble? He who, penetrating into the secrets of creation, arranges them under a formula which he proudly calls his scientific system? or he who, in the same pursuit, recognizes his glorious affinity with the Creator, and, in deepest gratitude for so sublime a birthright, strives to be the faithful interpreter of that Divine Intellect with whom he is permitted, nay, with whom he is intended, according to the laws of his being, to enter into communion? . . . if, in short, we can prove premeditation prior to the act of creation, we have done, once and for ever, with the desolate theory which refers us to the laws of matter as accounting for all the wonders of the universe, and leaves us with no God but the monotonous, unvarying action of physical forces, binding all things to their inevitable destiny. I think our science has now reached that degree of advancement, in which we may venture upon such an investigation. . . . I disclaim every intention of introducing in this work any evidence irrelevant to my subject, or of supporting any conclusions not immediately flowing from it; but I cannot overlook nor disregard here the close connection there is between the facts ascertained by scientific investigations, and the discussions now carried on respecting the origin of organized beings.

The more we look into his work, the more we realize that, in a sense, he did see the truth of Evolution. He had Darwin's facts before him and saw with different eyes the pattern they made. He saw metamorphosis. For Agassiz, evolution meant the growth of the embryo in the egg, the exfoliation of form from the inexplicable potential within the fusion of sperm and ovum. This was the classic sense of the word until the Darwinians applied it to the entire organic world. Where science now sees a linear development in time, Agassiz saw a lateral spread of design, somehow modified over long undulations of the eons, as Cuvier had suggested (possibly by the creation, no one knew how, of new species to replace extinct creatures), and somehow involved with the encroachment and recession of continental sheets of ice.

The Western world has had three students of metamorphosis: Ovid, Darwin, Picasso. Ovid took evolution on faith and metamorphosis for granted. Form flows into form. Eternal form, a god, must make his epiphany in matter. Beauty must manifest itself in beautiful things. Agassiz inherited this ancient idea: that within nature there is an intelligence, the force which the Greek perceived as a god, the force which Ovid as a poet saw expressed in the myths, a system of metaphors.

An oak leaf is a thought. It is a manifest idea. All of nature is some intelligent being's meditation on being. And on becoming, one might add, but we need not limit ourselves to that angle of vision. The becoming is not growth but transformation. Oak, acorn; acorn, oak. Agassiz saw that there are several maturations, not any one final fructification. In copulation we free a mature being, an animal we have carried in us, spermatozoon. He is little more than *Chaos Chaos*, an amoeba with a tail. Loosed, he (not us) goes to breed. He does what we agonize to do, what poem, song, and saint's meditation long for. He penetrates another being (or dies in crystal desiccation) and fuses with it. And here the succession of our metamorphoses begins. The fetus is a recapitulation of structural ideas, of themes in creation, an elaborate series of puns. Each stage is complete yet transitional; zygote is fetus to the child, anarchist and tyrant. The adolescent is not a recent child about to become an adult. He is completed, mature, with a life span, a mode of thought and response; he is, in fact, a separate animal. The child is to the adolescent, and the adolescent to the young man, as the tadpole to the frog. By being wholly psychological about this physical fact we have accumulated a fantasia of inadequate ideas and bruised our knowledge of reality.

At this point it may be worthwhile to indicate that Henry Adams saw in the science around him a hope that "sex and race" would at last be explained by trained minds, and he looked to a Clarence King and Raphael Pumpelly, Agassiz's second-generation men in the field, to correlate data. The world still waits. If the ideas on this page seem curious, the reader is invited to reflect that Agassiz, Pumpelly and King are scholars whose neglect is disturbing to contemplate. Agassiz died mid-career leaving a parabolic undertaking in scientific knowledge, and students are perfectly free to take up where he left off.

Growth, Agassiz saw, takes place *within* metamorphic form. The transformation of form into form is not properly growth but a true metamorphosis involving the total organism. There is no single growing up. The grown child metamorphoses into an adolescent (what understanding we might have if scientists would define these matters!); the adolescent into what classical wisdom called a *juventus*. Hence the boredom of a Spengler or a Frobenius, master analysts of metamorphic form and of the peculiar destinies inherent in form, with the tidy, insular minds of Darwin and Huxley, who wanted the interlocked natural systems of metamorphoses to be a progress (history is dramatic), a beautiful growth from one breathtakingly important—and accidental—egg, an exfoliation of all from a fortuity that held in potential the armadillo, the rose, the leopard, John Dillinger and Confucius.

Agassiz was not bored by Darwin; one wonders what a complex of certainty and doubt sometimes appeared to Agassiz's intelligence that never found expression. Spengler's finding Darwin insular derives from an inspection of the form of ideas, and ultimately, at our remove, it is precisely the characteristic contours of ideas which can lead us to an understanding of the nineteenth-century heritage we are still struggling to understand and to modify.

Ovid studied men turning into animals; Darwin, animals into men. Between these two brilliantly imaginative perceptions the subject of metamorphosis stands as one of the most lyric of natural facts. With one gesture nature holds matter firmly within her patterns. *Gingko biloba,* the oldest of surviving trees and high among the loveliest, is of a design so primeval that nothing but ferns and slimes are so antique. Yet it is a *Stammvater* tree, an archaic and oriental kinsman of the conifers. In Darwin's great vision of descent it was fit and survived, and so were its cedar and loblolly and fir cousins; that is, it is within a linear metamorphosis, branching into a deltoid pedigree, but most of all in deep time, a metamorphosis eons long.

For Agassiz, who discovered the Ice Age, time was no strange subject. But in the puzzle of seeming Ur-parents and infinitely varied descendants he was more modern. He belongs to the spirit of Picasso and Tchelitchew, who have meditated on change as infinite variety within a form, theme variations made at the very beginning of creation, simultaneous. The ideas of nature were for Agassiz what an image is for Picasso. Genus and species are perhaps ideal forms from which nature matures all the possibilities. Time need not enter into the discussion. Snake and bird and pteridactyl all came from the same workshop, from the same *materia* available to the craftsman; they do not need to be seen as made out of each other. An artist fascinated by a structural theme made them all. Darwin placed them in a time-order, and invited scientists to find the serpent halfway in metamorphosis toward being a pteridactyl, the pteridactyl becoming bird. Agassiz stood firm on the unshakable fact that dogs always have puppies; swans, cygnets; snakes, snakes. The *Origin of Species* was a misnomer. Darwin's *Metamorphoses* would have been better, but then Agassiz was a rival poet and fairly soon we may find both on the shelf with Ovid, splendors of imagination.

Ideas of nature are moral ideas. Darwin sat in black vastation, contemplating the god, or void, he could never decide which, that allowed to evolve from innocent matter such horrors as the tapeworm, the syphilis spirochaete, the poliomyelitis virus. Darwin's view was more macroscopic, of course; he was spared viruses, though by the end of his days optics were disclosing the subtle murderers. Darwin felt black enough about the way of a cat with a captured mouse.

We can detect in Agassiz, a notoriously good-natured man, a certain evasion in his taking a medical degree, to please his parents, and never looking at a patient. All applied science was repugnant to him. It was his calling to study the nature of reality. Lesser, practical men could fit knowledge to use. In these last days of the world we regard such an attitude with cold respect; we cannot be enthusiastic about it. Darwin was hurt that his theory destroyed faith. Was his plan of creation not as marvelous as Genesis? Was myth to be preferred to demonstrable truth? Agassiz's god we know less about. At least the eloquent intelligence discernible in nature was a palpable attribute of God. We do not anywhere find Agassiz an agnostic; we cannot discover any conflict in him between religion and science.

V. RADIANCE

> I have devoted my whole life to the study of Nature, and yet a single sentence may express all that I have done. I have shown that there is a correspondence between the succession of fishes in geological times and the different stages of their growth in the egg—that is all.
>
> *Methods of Study in Natural History*

But Agassiz adds: "It chanced to be a result that was found to apply to other groups and has led to other conclusions of a like nature." The method whereby Agassiz got from ignorance to knowledge of the Devonian and Silurian fossils to "other conclusions" was simply comparison. "The comparative method" is Agassiz's heritage, a discipline which filled American classrooms with scientists for two generations afterward and which has borne other fruit.

When Emerson, of all people, complained that Agassiz was emphasizing science to the detriment of Harvard as a university, Agassiz patiently replied that the rest of the curriculum should be brought up to the standards he had set for his zoology labs. "The education of a naturalist now consists chiefly in learning how to compare," Agassiz said (and the *now* is ominous). "By the same process the most mature results of scientific research in Philology, in Ethnology, and in Physical Science are reached."

The brilliant strokes of the intellect can be seen best in generalizations, in finding "the great laws of combination," but first the facts must be collected. Hence the diligence of the next generation, almost invariably Agassiz's pupils, in the field. Henry Adams has left us pictures of Clarence King in the Montana wilderness, and Pumpelly has left his own fine record of geologizing the world over. These two bring the matter of Agassiz's teaching into focus, for neither was his pupil; they took his inspiration from the air, and yet both acknowledge his leadership as if they had been his closest assistants.

Agassiz's influence has flowed beyond science, as he himself suggested that it might. If any man has repaid America's debt to Europe for giving us Agassiz, it is Ezra Pound, who, as we have seen, has acknowledged *his* debt to Agassiz. By transposing Agassiz's comparative method for critical use in literature, Pound created an extraordinary richness in contemporary criticism. In Pound's *The ABC of Reading* we find:

> The proper METHOD for studying poetry and good letters is the method of contemporary biologists, that is careful first-hand examination of the matter and continual COMPARISON of one "slide" or specimen with another.
>
> No man is equipped for modern thinking until he has understood the anecdote of Agassiz and the fish:
>
> A post-graduate student equipped with honors and diplomas went to Agassiz to receive the final and finishing touches. The great man offered him a sunfish and told him to describe it.
>
> Post-Graduate Student: "That's only a sunfish."
>
> Agassiz: "I know that. Write a description of it."
>
> After a few minutes the student returned with the description of the Ichthus Heliodiplodokus, or whatever term is used to conceal the common sunfish from vulgar knowledge, family of Heliichtherinkus, etc., as found in textbooks of the subject.
>
> Agassiz again told the student to describe the fish.
>
> The student produced a four-page essay. Agassiz then told him to look at the fish. At the end of three weeks the fish was in an advanced state of decomposition, but the student knew something about it.

When Pound completed and edited Ernest Fenollosa's *The Chinese Written Character as a Medium for Poetry*, he already had an intuitive grasp of Agassiz's intellectual heritage and saw in Fenollosa's inspection of Chinese poetry exactly the method which Agassiz had recommended to Emerson. Throughout Pound's critical work the guidelines suggested by Agassiz are discernible, and from this effort more brilliant ideas have been exposed than literary history will be able to follow up in a generation of scholars. Hence in the *Paradiso* of *The Cantos:*

Out of von Humboldt: Agassiz, Del Mar and Frobenius

Humboldt's *Kosmos* is still good reading, though, as with Agassiz, scholars give us biographies which generate interest in texts that remain unprinted and oftentimes inaccessible. "Agassiz never appeared to better advantage," Emerson wrote in his *Journal* in 1870, "as in his Biographical Discourse on Humboldt, at the Music Hall in Boston. . . . What is unusual for him, he read a written discourse, about two hours long; yet all of it strong, nothing to spare, not a weak point, no rhetoric, no falsetto; —his personal recollections and anecdotes of their intercourse, simple, frank, and tender in the tone of voice, too, no error of egotism or self-assertion, and far enough from French sentimentalism. He is quite as good a man as his hero, and not to be duplicated, I fear." Emerson the next year would include Agassiz among his Carlylean heroes ("My men"). Emerson could understand Agassiz as the heir of Humboldt and Cuvier (toward the end we find Agassiz looking to Baer the embryologist as his preceptor and writing in his introduction to the American edition of Hugh Miller's *Footprints of the Creator* that the next significant discoveries would have to be in embryology[4]) because he habitually saw genius as a spiritual gift from teacher to pupil. Behind "Out of von Humboldt: Agassiz . . ." there is a perception of radiant intelligence, certain qualities of humanity, a signature of the analytical faculties in concert with the searching mind.

Agassiz was a graft, analogous perhaps to Conrad in the history of the English novel. Japan had Lafcadio Hearn, Pum-

---

[4] Throughout the first edition of *The Origin of Species*, Darwin, whose German was notoriously shaky, made the Freudian error of writing Agassiz when he meant von Baer. This was shamefacedly corrected in later editions, but it tells us where Darwin was actually getting his knowledge of embryology. See Jane Oppenheimer, "An Embryological Enigma in *The Origin of Species*," in *Forerunners of Darwin 1745-1859*, ed. Glass, Temkin, and Straus, Johns Hopkins Press, 1959, pp. 292-322.

pelly and Ernest Fenollosa, and from them learned to teach, to mine ores, and to splice a long tradition to a neglectful present, but each of these scholars enlisted native genius. Their task was not so much transformation as directing energy, catalyzing. Agassiz transformed Harvard from college to university, but the bulk of his contribution he brought with him: a detailed knowledge of nature which Darwin envied, which upset the settled conclusions of lesser investigators. Agassiz focused his transforming powers on the student; it was as a teacher that he wished most to be remembered. His colleagues he urged to think as they would, within the capacities of a temperament which, inherited by Alexander Agassiz and aggravated by America, ran to horsewhipping utter strangers "for looking insolent," and pulling incautious drivers from the first automobiles and shaking them until their teeth rattled.

In an age of touchy formalities and pathological restrictions of spirit, Agassiz insisted that the teacher was both a dedicated scholar and a good-natured human being. The Agassiz intellect was as admirably liberal in its commerce with the world as intense and uncompromising in scholarship. Agassiz's father, Benjamin Rodolphe, hunted on Sabbath mornings, leaving his game and fowling-piece at the church door while he preached to his congregation at Motier, on Lake Morat. Agassiz himself broke every smoking rule at Harvard, fenced with his students, and once offered the Emperor of Brazil an assistant's position at the university museum.

Scholarship, imagination, energy, intellect, good nature. Theodore Lyman, watching the Harvard students bearing Agassiz's heavy casket to the chapel in the Yard, said: "He was younger than any of them."

Acknowledgments

I am indebted to Eva Thurman who gave me a copy of the *Contributions* bound in Neptune blue; to Sally Sylk who typed the manuscript; to my students, Steve Berrien and Ted Hauri, for their generosity in doing various chores; and to Karl Hill, for his patience, and for his suggesting that I prepare the book. I am grateful to Robert Butman for reminding me that Raphael Pumpelly had Hugh Miller read to him as a child.

I.
Essay on Classification

Note

The great "Essay on Classification," standing as both introduction and base to the projected but, after four magnificent volumes, uncompleted *Contributions to the Natural History of the United States,* is Agassiz's masterpiece of analytical and theoretical writing. For detail and sheer weight of research his work on fossil and fresh-water fishes is, all things considered, a greater achievement than the "Essay," just as the three volumes of the *Contributions* are a greater work than the general plan which they are intended to illustrate. For permanent value to science, his work, which does not have to be emended by modern thought, is less embarrassed than the "Essay" by the truths of evolution. But the "Essay" is the epitome of Agassiz's thought and without it his mind is but that of a brilliant zoologist and pioneer geologist. Here he presents firmly the structure of nature as he sees it, not as he thinks it is, as he insists, but as it actually is: the scheme of an ultimate intelligence, logical and coherent.

Read as the firm argument to a work of scope and infinite detail, it is impressive in its brevity and conciseness. A mind of lesser knowledge would have needed more words, more qualifiers hedging every assertion. Agassiz wrote briefly because he wrote with authority, and he wrote simply and clearly because his ideas were compressed, dependable in use, unwobbling.

This severe, calm essay was intended to stand unscathed against Darwinian theory. Its beauty as one side of a polemic is that it would have been the same had Darwin not written a word. In this there is dignity and courage, generating no irony (for us), and no confusion. The four volumes of the *Contributions* remain among the finest of American books, an unchallengeable masterwork of observation and analysis, alone in its ambitions and lonely in its integrity, tragic in its incompletion.

From the text here presented there have been removed the scientific notes which listed sources, suggested research, and stood as evidence of the diligence with which Agassiz worked. It would be costly and quixotic to reprint these systems of clues, wonderous compilations of abbreviated titles and page references, displaying heroic energy and erudition, though they are very much a part of the subject, and the scientific mind will wince to see them missing.

The selection reprinted here consists of the first eighteen parts of the essay; that is, the main argument up until it branches into technicalities beyond the interest of the common reader, and is roughly half of the whole work.

I. Essay on Classification

SECTIONS I-XVIII

from *Contributions to the Natural History*
of the United States of America, 1857

CHAPTER FIRST.

The Fundamental Relations of Animals
to One Another and to the World
in Which They Live, as the Basis
of the Natural System of Animals.

SECTION I: *The Leading Features of a Natural Zoologi-*
cal System Are All Founded in Nature.

Modern classifications of animals and plants are based upon
the peculiarities of their structure; and this is generally considered as the most important, if not the only safe, guide in our
attempts to determine the natural relations which exist between
animals. This view of the subject seems to me, however, to cir-
cumscribe the foundation of a natural system of Zoology and
Botany within too narrow limits, to exclude from our consideration some of the most striking characteristics of the two organic
kingdoms of nature, and to leave it doubtful how far the arrangement thus obtained is founded in reality, and how far it is merely
the expression of our estimate of these structural differences. It
has appeared to me appropriate, therefore, to present here a
short exposition of the leading features of the animal kingdom, as

31

types among Vertebrata—as it would afford a desirable opportunity of establishing a standard of comparison between the changes animals undergo during their growth, and the permanent characters of full-grown individuals of other types, and, perhaps, of showing also what other points beside structure might with advantage be considered in ascertaining the manifold relations of animals to one another and to the world in which they live, upon which the natural system may be founded.

In considering these various topics, I shall of necessity have to discuss many questions bearing upon the very origin of organized beings, and to touch upon many points now under discussion among scientific men. I shall, however, avoid controversy as much as possible, and only try to render the results of my own studies and meditations in as clear a manner as I possibly can in the short space that I feel justified in devoting to this subject in this volume.

There is no question in Natural History on which more diversified opinions are entertained than on that of Classification; not that naturalists disagree as to the necessity of some sort of arrangement in describing animals or plants, for since nature has become the object of special studies, it has been the universal aim of all naturalists to arrange the objects of their investigations in the most natural order possible. Even Buffon, who began the publication of his great Natural History by denying the existence in nature of any thing like a system, closed his work by grouping the birds according to certain general features, exhibited in common by many of them. It is true, authors have differed in their estimation of the characters on which their different arrangements are founded; and it is equally true that they have not viewed their arrangements in the same light, some having plainly acknowledged the artificial character of their systems, while others have urged theirs as the true expression of the natural relations which exist between the objects themselves. But, whether systems were presented as artificial or natural, they have, to this day, been considered generally as the expression of man's understanding of natural objects, and not as a system devised by the Supreme Intelligence, and manifested in these objects.[1]

[Footnotes for Part I will be found on page 108.]

There is only one point in these innumerable systems on which all seem to meet, namely, the existence in nature of distinct species, persisting with all their peculiarities, for a time at least; for even the immutability of species has been questioned. Beyond species, however, this confidence in the existence of the divisions, generally admitted in zoological systems, diminishes greatly.

With respect to genera, we find already the number of the naturalists who accept them as natural divisions much smaller; few of them having expressed a belief that genera have as distinct an existence in nature as species. And as to families, orders, classes, or any kind of higher divisions, they seem to be universally considered as convenient devices, framed with the view of facilitating the study of innumerable objects, and of grouping them in the most suitable manner. The indifference with which this part of our science is generally treated becomes unjustifiable, considering the progress which Zoology in general has made of late. It is a matter of consequence, whether genera are circumscribed in our systematic works within these or those limits; whether families inclose a wider or more contracted range of genera; whether such or such orders are admitted in a class, and what are the natural boundaries of classes; as well as how the classes themselves are related to one another, and whether all these groups are considered as resting upon the same foundation in nature or not.

Without venturing here upon an analysis of the various systems of Zoology—the prominent features of which are sufficiently exemplified for my purpose by the systems of Linnaeus and Cuvier, which must be familiar to every student of Natural History—it is certainly a seasonable question to ask, whether the animal kingdom exhibits only those few subdivisions into orders and genera which the Linnaean system indicates, or whether the classes differ among themselves to the extent which the system of Cuvier would lead us to suppose. Or is, after all, this complicated structure of Classification merely an ingenious human invention, which every one may shape, as he pleases, to suit himself? When we remember that all the works on Natural History admit some system or other of this kind, it is certainly an aim worthy of a true naturalist, to ascertain what is the real meaning of all these divisions.

Embryology, moreover, forces the inquiry upon us at every step, as it is impossible to establish precise comparisons between the different stages of growth of young animals of any higher group and the permanent characters of full-grown individuals of other types, without first ascertaining what is the value of the divisions with which we may have to compare embryos. This is my reason for introducing here, in a work chiefly devoted to Embryology, a subject to which I have paid the most careful attention for many years past, and for the solution of which I have made special investigations.

Before I proceed any further, however, I would submit one case to the consideration of my reader. Suppose that the innumerable articulated animals, which are counted by tens of thousands, nay, perhaps by hundreds of thousands, had never made their appearance upon the surface of our globe, with one single exception: that, for instance, our Lobster (*Homarus americanus*) were the only representative of that extraordinarily diversified type—how should we introduce that species of animals in our systems? Simply as a genus with one species, by the side of all the other classes with their orders, families, etc., or as a family containing only one genus with one species, or as a class with one order and one genus, or as a class with one family and one genus? And should we acknowledge, by the side of Vertebrata, Mollusks, and Radiata, another type of Articulata, on account of the existence of that one Lobster, or would it be natural to call him by a single name, simply as a species, in contradistinction to all other animals? It was the consideration of this supposed case which led me to the investigations detailed below, which, I hope, may end in the ultimate solution of this apparently inextricable question.

Though what I have now to say about this supposed case cannot be fully appreciated before reading my remarks in the following chapter, respecting the character of the different kinds of groups adopted in our systems, it must be obvious that our Lobster, to be what we see these animals are, must have its frame constructed upon that very same plan of structure which it exhibits now; and, if I should succeed in showing that there is a difference between the conception of a plan and the manner of its execution, upon which classes are founded in contradistinction to the types to which they belong, we might arrive at this distinction by a careful investigation of that single Articulate, as well as by the study of all of them; and we might then recognize its types and ascertain its class characters as fully as if the type embraced several classes, and this class thousands of species. Then that animal has a form, which no one would fail to recognize; so that, if form can be shown to be characteristic of families, we could thus determine its family. Again: besides the general structure, showing the fundamental relations of all the systems of organs of the body to one another in their natural development, our investigation could be carried into the study of the details of that structure in every part, and thus lead to the recognition of what constitutes everywhere generic characters. Finally: as this animal has definite relations to the surrounding world, as the individuals living at the time bear definite relations to one another, as the parts of their body show definite proportions, and as the surface of the body exhibits a special ornamentation, the specific characters could be traced as fully as if a number of other species were at hand for comparison; and they might be drawn and described with sufficient accuracy to distinguish it at any future time from any other set of species found afterwards, however closely these new species might be allied to it. In this case, then, we should have to acknowledge a separate branch in the animal kingdom, with a class, a family, and a genus, to introduce one species to its proper place in the system of animals. But the class would have no order, if orders determine the rank, as ascertained by the complication of structure; for, where there is but one representative of a type, there is no room for the question of its superiority or inferiority in comparison to others within the limits of the class, orders being groups subordinate to one another in their class. Yet, even in this case, the question of the standing of Articulata, as a type among the other great branches of the animal kingdom, would be open to our investigations; but it would assume another aspect from that which it now presents, as the comparison of Articulata with the other types would then be limited to the Lobster, and would lead to a very different result from that to which we may arrive, now that this type includes such a large number of most extensively diversified representatives, belonging even to different classes. That such speculations are not idle must be apparent to any one who is aware, that, during every period in the history of our globe in past geological ages,[2] the general relations, the numeric proportions, and the relative importance of all the types of the animal kingdom, have been ever changing, until their present relations were established. Here, then, the individuals of one species, as observed while living, simultaneously exhibit characters, which, to be expressed satisfactorily and in conformity to what nature tells us, would require the establishment, not only of a distinct species, but also of a distinct genus, a distinct family, a distinct class, a distinct branch. Is not this in itself evidence enough that genera, families, orders, classes, and types have the same foundation in nature as species, and that the individuals living at the time have alone a material existence, they being the bearers, not only of all these different categories of structure upon which the natural system of animals is founded, but also of all the relations which animals sustain to the surrounding world—thus showing that species do not exist in nature in a different way from the higher groups, as is so generally believed?

The divisions of animals according to branch, class, order, family, genus, and species, by which we express the results of our investigations into the relations of the animal kingdom, and which constitute the first question respecting the scientific systems of Natural History which we have to consider, seem to me to deserve the consideration of all thoughtful minds. Are these divisions artificial or natural? Are they the devices of the human mind to classify and arrange our knowledge in such a manner as to bring it more readily within our grasp and facilitate further investigations, or have they been instituted by the Divine Intelligence as the categories of his mode of thinking?[3] Have we, perhaps, thus far been only the unconscious interpreters of a Divine conception, in our attempts to expound nature? and when, in our pride of philosophy, we thought that we were inventing systems of science and classifying creation by the force of our own reason, have we followed only, and reproduced, in our imperfect expressions, the plan whose foundations were laid in the dawn of creation, and the development of which we are laboriously studying—thinking, as we put together and arrange our fragmentary knowledge, that we are anew introducing order into chaos? Is this order the result of the exertions of human skill and ingenuity, or is it inherent in the objects themselves, so that the intelligent student of Natural History is led unconsciously, by the study of the animal kingdom itself, to these conclusions, the great divisions under which he arranges animals being indeed but the headings to the chapters of the great book which he is reading? To me it appears indisputable, that this order and arrangement of our studies are based upon the natural, primitive relations of animal life—those systems, to which we have given the names of the great leaders of our science who first proposed them, being in truth but translations, into human language, of the thoughts of the Creator. And if this is indeed so, do we not find in this adaptability of the human intellect to the facts of creation, by which we become instinctively, and, as I have said, unconsciously, the translators of the thoughts of God, the most conclusive proof of our affinity with the Divine Mind? and is not this intellectual and spiritual connection with the Almighty worthy our deepest consideration? If there is any truth in the belief that man is made in the image of God, it is surely not amiss for the philosopher to endeavor, by the study of his own mental operations, to approximate the workings of the Divine Reason, learning, from the nature of his own mind, better to understand the Infinite Intellect from which it is derived. Such a suggestion may, at first sight, appear irreverent. But, which is the truly humble? He who, penetrating into the secrets of creation, arranges them under a formula which he proudly calls his scientific system? or he who, in the same pursuit, recognizes his glorious affinity with the Creator, and, in deepest gratitude for so sublime a birthright, strives to be the faithful interpreter of that Divine Intellect with whom he is permitted, nay, with whom he is intended, according to the laws of his being, to enter into communion?

I confess that this question as to the nature and foundation of our scientific classifications appears to me to have the deepest importance, an importance far greater indeed than is usually attached to it. If it can be proved that man has not invented, but only traced this systematic arrangement in nature, that these relations and proportions which exist throughout the animal and vegetable world have an intellectual, an ideal connection in the mind of the Creator, that this plan of creation, which so commends itself to our highest wisdom, has not grown out of the necessary action of physical laws, but was the free conception of the Almighty Intellect, matured in his thought, before it was manifested in tangible external forms—if, in short, we can prove premeditation prior to the act of creation, we have done, once and for ever, with the desolate theory which refers us to the laws of matter as accounting for all the wonders of the universe, and leaves us with no God but the monotonous, unvarying action of physical forces, binding all things to their inevitable destiny.[4] I think our science has now reached that degree of advancement, in which we may venture upon such an investigation.

The argument for the existence of an intelligent Creator is generally drawn from the adaptation of means to ends, upon which the Bridgewater treatises, for example, have been based. But this does not appear to me to cover the whole ground, for we can conceive that the natural action of objects upon each other should result in a final fitness of the universe, and thus produce an harmonious whole; nor does the argument derived from the connection of organs and functions seem to me more satisfactory, for, beyond certain limits, it is not even true. We find organs without functions, as, for instance, the teeth of the whale, which never cut through the gum, the breast in all males of the class of mammalia; these and similar organs are preserved in obedience to a certain uniformity of fundamental structure, true to the original formula of that division of animal life, even when not essential to its mode of existence. The organ remains, not for the performance of a function, but with reference to a plan, and might almost remind us of what we often see in human structures, when, for instance, in architecture, the same external combinations are retained for the sake of symmetry and harmony of proportion, even when they have no practical object.

I disclaim every intention of introducing in this work any evidence irrelevant to my subject, or of supporting any conclusions not immediately flowing from it; but I cannot overlook nor disregard here the close connection there is between the facts ascertained by scientific investigations, and the discussions now carried on respecting the origin of organized beings. And though I know those who hold it to be very unscientific to believe that thinking is not something inherent in matter, and that there is an essential difference between inorganic and living and thinking beings, I shall not be prevented by any such pretensions of a false philosophy from expressing my conviction that as long as it cannot be shown that matter or physical forces do actually reason, I shall consider any manifestation of thought as evidence of the existence of a thinking being as the author of such thought, and shall look upon an intelligent and intelligible connection between the facts of nature as direct proof of the existence of a thinking God,[5] as certainly as man exhibits the power of thinking when he recognizes their natural relations.

As I am not writing a didactic work, I will not enter here into a detailed illustration of the facts relating to the various subjects submitted to the consideration of my reader, beyond what is absolutely necessary to follow the argument, nor dwell at any length upon the conclusions to which they lead, but simply recall the leading features of the evidence, assuming in the argument a full acquaintance with the whole range of data upon which it is founded, whether derived from the affinities or the anatomical structure of animals, or from their habits and their geographical distribution, from their embryology, or from their succession in past geological ages, and the peculiarities they have exhibited during each, believing, as I do, that isolated and disconnected facts are of little consequence in the contemplation of the whole plan of creation, and that without a consideration of all the facts furnished by the study of the habits of animals, by their anatomy, their embryology, and the history of the past ages of our globe, we shall never arrive at the knowledge of the natural system of animals.

Let us now consider some of these topics more specially.

SECTION II: *Simultaneous Existence of the Most Diversified Types under Identical Circumstances.*

It is a fact which seems to be entirely overlooked by those who assume an extensive influence of physical causes upon the very existence of organized beings, that the most diversified types of animals and plants are everywhere found under identical circumstances. The smallest sheet of fresh water, every point upon the seashore, every acre of dry land, teems with a variety of animals and plants. The narrower the boundaries are, which may be assigned as the primitive home of all these beings, the more uniform must be the conditions under which they are assumed to have originated; so uniform, indeed, that in the end the inference would be, that the same physical causes could produce the most diversified effects.[6] To concede, on the contrary, that these organisms may have appeared in the beginning over a wide area, is to grant, at the same time, that the physical influences under which they existed at first were not so specific as to justify the assumption that these could be the cause of their appearance. In whatever connection, then, the first appearance of organized beings upon earth is viewed, whether it is assumed that they originated within the most limited areas, or over the widest range of their present natural geographical distribution, animals and plants being everywhere diversified to the most extraordinary extent, it is plain that the physical influences under which they subsist cannot logically be considered as the cause of that diversity. In this, as in every other respect, when considering the relations of animals and plants to the conditions under which they live, or to one another, we are inevitably led to look beyond the material facts of the case for an explanation of their existence. Those who have taken another view of this subject, have mistaken the action and reaction which exist everywhere between organized beings, and the physical influences under which they live for a causal or genetic connection, and carried their mistake so far as to assert that these manifold influences could really extend to the production of these beings; not considering how inadequate such a cause would be, and that even the action of physical agents upon organized beings presupposes the very existence of those beings. The simple fact that there has been a period in the history of our earth, now well known to geologists,[7] when none of these organized beings as yet existed, and when, nevertheless, the material constitution of our globe, and the physical forces acting upon it, were essentially the same as they are now, shows that those influences are insufficient to call into existence any living being.

Physicists know, indeed, these physical agents more accurately than the naturalists, who ascribe to them the origin of organized beings; let us then ask them, whether the nature of these agents is not specific, whether their mode of action is not specific? They will all answer, that they are. Let us further inquire of them, what evidence there is, in the present state of our knowledge, that at any time these physical agents have produced any thing they no longer do produce, and what probability there is that they may ever have produced any organized being? If I am not greatly mistaken, the masters in that department of science will, one and all, answer, none whatever.

But the character of the connections between organized beings and the physical conditions under which they live is such as to display thought; these connections are therefore to be considered as established, determined, and regulated by a thinking being. They must have been fixed for each species at its beginning, while the fact of their permanency through successive generations is further evidence that with their natural relations to the surrounding world were also determined the relations of individuals to one another, their generic as well as their family relations, and every higher grade of affinity, showing, therefore, not only thought, in reference to the physical conditions of existence, but such comprehensive thoughts as would embrace simultaneously every characteristic of each species.

Every fact relating to the geographical distribution of animals and plants might be alluded to in confirmation of this argument, but especially the character of every fauna and every flora upon the surface of the globe. How great the diversity of animals and plants living together in the same region may be, can be ascertained by the perusal of special works upon the Zoology and Botany of different countries, or from special treatises upon the geographical distribution of animals and plants. I need, therefore, not enter into further details upon this subject, especially since it is discussed more fully below.

It might, perhaps, be urged, that animals living together in exceptional conditions, and exhibiting structural peculiarities apparently resulting from these conditions, such as the blind fish, the blind crawfish, and the blind insects of the Mammoth Cave in Kentucky, furnish uncontrovertible evidence of the immediate influence of those exceptional conditions upon the organs of vision. If this, however, were the case, how does it happen that that remarkable fish, the *Amblyopsis speloeus*, has only such remote affinities to other fishes? Or were, perhaps, the sum of influences at work to make that fish blind, capable also of devising such a combination of structural characters as that fish has in common with all other fishes, with those peculiarities which at the same time distinguish it? Does not, rather, the existence of a rudimentary eye discovered by Dr. J. Wyman in the blind fish show that these animals, like all others, were created with all their peculiarities by the fiat of the Almighty, and this rudiment of eyes left them as a remembrance of the general plan of structure of the great type to which they belong? Or will, perhaps, some one of those naturalists who know so much better than the physicists what physical forces may produce, and that they may produce, and have produced every living being known, explain also to us why subterraneous caves in America produce blind fishes, blind crustacea, and blind insects, while in Europe they produce nearly blind reptiles? If there is no thought in the case, why is it, then, that this very reptile, the *Proteus anguinus*, forms, with a number of other reptiles living in North America and in Japan, one of the most natural series known in the animal kingdom, every member of which exhibits a distinct grade in the scale?

After we have freed ourselves from the mistaken impression that there may be some genetic connection between physical forces and organized beings, there remains a vast field of investigation to ascertain the true relations between both, to their full extent, and within their natural limits. A mere reference to the mode of breathing of different types of animals, and to their organs of locomotion, which are more particularly concerned in these relations, will remind every naturalist of how great importance in classification is the structure of these parts, and how much better they might be understood in this point of view, were the different structures of these organs more extensively studied in their direct reference to the world in which animals live. If this had been done, we should no longer call by the same common name of legs and wings organs so different as the locomotive appendages of the insects and those of the birds? We should no longer call lungs the breathing cavity of snails, as well as the air pipes of mammalia, birds, and reptiles? A great reform is indeed needed in this part of our science, and no study can prepare us better for it than the investigation of the mutual dependence of the structure of animals, and the conditions in which they live.

SECTION III: *Repetition of Identical Types under the Most Diversified Circumstances.*

As much as the diversity of animals and plants living under identical physical conditions shows the independence of organized beings from the medium in which they dwell, so far as their origin is concerned, so independent do they appear again from the same influences when we consider the fact that identical types occur everywhere upon earth under the most diversified circumstances. If we sum up all these various influences and conditions of existence under the common appellation of cosmic influences, or of physical causes, or of climate in the widest sense of the word, and then look around us for the extreme differences in that respect upon the whole surface of the globe, we find still the most similar, nay identical types (and I allude here, under the expression of type, to the most diversified acceptations of the word) living normally under their action. There is no structural difference between the herrings of the Arctic, or those of the Temperate zone, or those of the Tropics, or those of the Antarctic regions; there are not any more between the foxes and wolves of the most distant parts of the globe. Moreover, if there were any, and the specific differences existing between them were insisted upon, could any relation between these differences and the cosmic influences under which they live be pointed out, which would at the same time account for the independence of their structure in general? Or, in other words, how could it be assumed that while these causes would produce specific differences, they would at the same time produce generic identity, family identity, ordinal identity, class identity, typical identity? Identity in every thing that is truly important, high, and complicated in the structure of animals, produced by the most diversified influences, while at the same time extreme physical differences, considered as the cause of the existence of these animals, would produce diversity in secondary relations only! What logic!

Does not all this show, on the contrary, that organized beings exhibit the most astonishing independence of the physical causes under which they live; an independence so great that it can only be understood as the result of a power governing these physical causes as well as the existence of animals and plants, and bringing all into harmonious relations by adaptations which never can be considered as cause and effect?

When naturalists have investigated the influence of physical causes upon living beings, they have constantly overlooked the fact that the features which are thus modified are only of secondary importance in the life of animals and plants, and that neither the plan of their structure, nor the various complications of that structure, are ever affected by such influences. What, indeed, are the parts of the body which are, in any way, affected by external influences? Chiefly those which are in immediate contact with the external world, such as the skin, and in the skin chiefly its outer layers, its color, the thickness of the fur, the color of the hair, the feathers, and the scales; then the size of the body and its weight, as far as it is dependent on the quality and quantity of the food; the thickness of the shell of Mollusks, when they live in waters or upon a soil containing more or less limestone, etc.

The rapidity or slowness of the growth is also influenced in a measure by the course of the seasons, in different years; so is also the fecundity, the duration of life, etc. But all this has nothing to do with the essential characteristics of animals.

A book has yet to be written upon the independence of organized beings of physical causes, as most of what is generally ascribed to the influence of physical agents upon organized beings ought to be considered as a connection established between them in the general plan of creation.

SECTION IV: *Unity of Plan in Otherwise Highly Diversified Types.*

Nothing is more striking throughout the animal and vegetable kingdoms than the unity of plan in the structure of the most diversified types. From pole to pole, in every longitude, mammalia, birds, reptiles, and fishes, exhibit one and the same plan of structure, involving abstract conceptions of the highest order, far transcending the broadest generalizations of man, for it is only after the most laborious investigations man has arrived at an imperfect understanding of this plan. Other plans, equally wonderful, may be traced in Articulata, in Mollusks, in Radiata, and in the various types of plants, and yet this logical connection, these beautiful harmonies, this infinite diversity in unity are represented by some as the result of forces exhibiting no trace of intelligence, no power of thinking, no faculty of combination, no knowledge of time and space. If there is any thing which places man above all other beings in nature, it is precisely the circumstance that he possesses those noble attributes without which, in their most exalted excellence and perfection, not one of these general traits of relationship so characteristic of the great types of the animal and vegetable kingdoms, can be understood, or even perceived. How, then, could these relations have been devised without similar powers? If all these relations are almost beyond the reach of the mental powers of man, and if man himself is part and parcel of the whole system, how could this system have been called into existence if there does not exist One Supreme Intelligence, as the Author of all things?

SECTION V: *Correspondence in the Details of Structure in Animals Otherwise Entirely Disconnected.*

During the first decade of this century, naturalists began to study relations among animals which had escaped almost entirely the attention of earlier observers. Though Aristotle knew already that the scales of fishes correspond to the feathers of birds, it is but recently that anatomists have discovered the close correspondence which exists between all the parts of all animals belonging to the same type, however different they may appear at first sight. Not only is the wing of the bird indentical in its structure with the arm of man, or the fore leg of a quadruped, it agrees quite as closely with the fin of the whale, or the pectoral fin of the fish, and all these together correspond in the same manner with their hind extremities. Quite as striking a coincidence is observed between the solid skull-box, the immovable bones of the face and the lower jaw of man and the other mammalia, and the structure of the bony frame of the head of birds, turtles, lizards, snakes, frogs, and fishes. But this correspondence is not limited to the skeleton; every other system of organs exhibits in these animals the same relations, the same identity in plan and structure, whatever be the difference in the form of the parts, in their number, and even in their functions. Such an agreement in the structure of animals is called their homology, and is more or less close in proportion as the animals in which it is traced are more or less nearly related.

The same agreement exists between the different systems and their parts in Articulata, in Mollusks, and in Radiata, only that their structure is built up upon respectively different plans, though in these three types the homologies have not yet been traced to the same extent as among Vertebrata. There is therefore still a wide field open for investigations in this most attractive branch of Zoology. So much, however, is already plain from what has been done in this department of our science, that the identity of structure among animals does not extend to all the four branches of the animal kingdom; that, on the contrary, every great type is constructed upon a distinct plan, so peculiar, indeed, that homologies cannot be extended from one type to the other, but are strictly limited within each of them. The more remote resemblance which may be traced between representatives of different types, is founded upon analogy, and not upon affinity. While, for instance, the head of fishes exhibits the most striking homology with that of reptiles, birds, and mammalia, as a whole, as well as in all its parts, that of Articulata is only analogous to it and to its part. What is commonly called head in Insects is not a head like that of Vertebrata; it has not a distinct cavity for the brain, separated from that which communicates below the neck with the chest and abdomen; its solid envelope does not consist of parts of an internal skeleton, surrounded by flesh, but is formed of external rings, like those of the body, soldered together; it contains but one cavity, which includes the cephalic ganglion, as well as the organs of the mouth, and all the muscles of the head. The same may be said of the chest, the legs and wings, the abdomen, and all the parts they contain. The cephalic ganglion is not homologous to the brain, nor are the organs of senses homologous to those of Vertebrata, even though they perform the same functions. The alimentary canal is formed in a very different way in the embryos of the two types, as are also their respiratory organs, and it is as unnatural to identify them, as it would be still to consider gills and lungs as homologous among Vertebrata now that embryology has taught us that in different stages of growth these two kinds of respiratory organs exist in all Vertebrata in very different organic connections one from the other.

What is true of the branch of Articulata when compared to that of Vertebrata, is equally true of the Mollusks and Radiata when compared with one another or with the two other types, as might easily be shown by a fuller illustration of the correspondence of their structure, within these limits. This inequality in the fundamental character of the structure of the four branches of the animal kingdom points to the necessity of a radical reform in the nomenclature of comparative anatomy. Some naturalists, however, have already extended such comparisons respecting the structure of animals beyond the limits pointed out by nature, when they have attempted to show that all structures may be reduced to one norm, and when they have maintained, for instance, that every bone existing in any Vertebrate must have its counterpart in every other species of that type. To assume such a uniformity among animals, would amount to denying to the Creator even as much freedom in expressing his thoughts as man enjoys.

If it be true, as pointed out above, that all animals are constructed upon four different plans of structure, in such a manner that all the different kinds of animals are only different expressions of these fundamental formulae, we may well compare the whole animal kingdom to a work illustrating four great ideas, between which there is no other connecting link than the unity exhibited in the eggs in which their most diversified manifestations are first embodied in an embryonic form, to undergo a series of transformations, and appear in the end in that wonderful variety of independent living beings which inhabit our globe, or have inhabited it from the earliest period of the existence of life upon its surface.

The most surprising feature of the animal kingdom seems, however, to me to rest neither in its diversity, nor in the close affinity of some of its representatives, while others are so different, nor in the manifold relations of all of them to one another and the surrounding world, but in the circumstance that beings endowed with such different and such unequal gifts should nevertheless constitute an harmonious whole, intelligibly connected in all its parts.

SECTION VI: *Various Degrees and Different kinds of Relationship among Animals.*

The degrees of relationship existing between different animals are most diversified. They are not only akin as representatives of the same species, bearing as such the closest resemblance to one another; different species may also be related as members of the same genus, the representatives of different genera may belong to the same family, and the same order may contain different families, the same class different orders, and the same type several classes. The existence of different degrees of affinity between animals and plants which have not the remotest genealogical connection, which live in the most distant parts of the world, which have existed in periods long gone by in the history of our earth, is a fact beyond dispute, at least, within certain limits, no longer controverted by well informed observers. Upon what can this be founded? Is it that the retentive capacity of the memory of the physical forces at work upon this globe is such, that after bringing forth a type according to one pattern, in the infancy of this earth, that pattern was adhered to under conditions, no matter how diversified, to reproduce, at another period, something similar, and so on, through all ages, until at the period of the establishment of the present state of things, all the infinitude of new animals and new plants which now crowd its surface, should be cast in these four moulds, in such a manner as to exhibit, notwithstanding their complicated relations to the surrounding world, all those more deeply seated general relations, which establish among them the different degrees of affinity we may trace so readily in all the representatives of the same type? Does all this really look more like the working of blind forces than like the creation of a reflective mind establishing deliberately all the categories of existence we recognize in nature, and combining them in that wonderful harmony which unites all things into such a perfect system, that even to read it, as it is established, or even with all the imperfections of a translation, should be considered as the highest achievement of the maturest genius?

Nothing seems to me to prove more directly and more fully the action of a reflective mind, to indicate more plainly a deliberate consideration of the subject, than the different categories upon which species, genera, families, orders, classes, and branches are founded in nature, and manifested in material reality in a succession of individuals, the life of which is limited in its duration to comparatively very short periods. The great wonder in these relations consists in the fugitive character of the bearers of this complicated harmony. For while species persist during long periods, the individuals which represent them are ever changing, one set dying after the other, in quick succession. Genera, it is true, may extend over longer periods, families, orders, and classes may even have existed during all periods during which animals have existed at all; but whatever may have been the duration of their existence, at all times these different divisions have stood in the same relation to one another and to their respective branches, and have always been represented upon our globe in the same manner, by a succession of ever renewed and short-lived individuals.

As, however, the second chapter of this work is entirely devoted to the consideration of the different kinds and the different degrees of affinity existing among animals, I will not enter here into any details upon this subject, but simply recall the fact that, in the course of time, investigators have agreed more and more with one another in their estimates of these relations, and built up systems more and more conformable to one another. This result, which is fully exemplified by the history of our science, is in itself sufficient to show that there is a system in nature to which the different systems of authors are successive approximations, more and more closely agreeing with it, in proportion as the human mind has understood nature better. This growing coincidence between our systems and that of nature shows further the identity of the operations of the human and the Divine intellect; especially when it is remembered to what an extraordinary degree many *a priori* conceptions, relating to nature, have in the end proved to agree with the reality, in spite of every objection at first offered by empiric observers.

SECTION VII: *Simultaneous Existence in the Earliest Geological Periods, of All the Great Types of Animals.*

It was formerly believed by geologists and palaeontologists that the lowest animals first made their appearance upon this globe, and that they were followed by higher and higher types, until man crowned the series. Every geological museum, representing at all the present state of our knowledge, may now furnish the evidence that this is not the case. On the contrary, representatives of numerous families belonging to all the four great branches of the animal kingdom, are well known to have existed simultaneously in the oldest geological formations. Nevertheless, I well remember when I used to hear the great geologists of the time assert, that the Corals were the first inhabitants of our globe, that Mollusks and Articulata followed in order, and that Vertebrates did not appear until long after these. What an extraordinary change the last thirty years have brought about in our knowledge, and the doctrines generally adopted respecting the existence of animals and plants in past ages! However much naturalists may still differ in their views regarding the origin, the gradation, and the affinities of animals, they now all know that neither Radiata, nor Mollusks, nor Articulata, have any priority one over the other, as to the time of their first appearance upon earth; and though some still maintain that Vertebrata originated somewhat later, it is universally conceded that they were already in existence toward the end of the first great epoch in the history of our globe. I think it would not be difficult to show upon physiological grounds that their presence upon earth dates from as early a period as any of the three other great types of the animal kingdom, since fishes exist wherever Radiata, Mollusks, and Articulata are found together, and the plan of structure of these four great types constitutes a system intimately connected in its very essence. Moreover, for the last twenty years, every extensive investigation among the oldest fossiliferous rocks has carried the origin of Vertebrata step by step further back, so that whatever may be the final solution of this vexed question, so much is already established by innumerable facts, that the idea of a gradual succession of Radiata, Mollusks, Articulata, and Vertebrata, is for ever out of the question. It is proved beyond doubt, that Radiata, Mollusca, and Articulata are everywhere found together in the oldest geological formations, and that very early Vertebrata are associated with them, to continue together through all geological ages to the present time. This shows that even in those early days of the existence of our globe, when its surface did not yet present those diversified features which it has exhibited in later periods, and which it exhibits in still greater variety now, animals belonging to all the great types now represented upon earth, were simultaneously called into existence. It shows, further, that unless the physical elements then at work could have devised such plans, and impressed them upon the material world as the pattern upon which Nature was to build for ever afterwards, no such general relations as exist among all animals, of all geological periods, as well as among those now living, could ever have existed.

This is not all: every class among Radiata, Mollusks, and Articulata, is known to have been represented in those earliest days, with the exception of the Acalephs[8] and Insects only. It is, therefore, not only the plan of the four great types which must have been adopted then, the manner in which these plans were to be executed, the systems of form under which these structures were to be clothed, even the ultimate details of structure which in different genera bear definite relations to those of other genera; the mode of differentiation of species, and the nature of their relations to the surrounding media, must likewise have been determined, as the character of the classes is as well defined as that of the four great branches of the animal kingdom, or that of the families, the genera, and the species. Again, the first representatives of each class stand in definite relations to their successors in later periods, and as their order of apparition corresponds to the various degrees of complication in their structure, and form natural series closely linked together, this natural gradation must have been contemplated from the very beginning. There can be the less doubt upon this point, as man, who comes last, closes in his own cycle a series, the gradation of which points from the very beginning to him as its last term. I think it can be shown by anatomical evidence that man is not only the last and highest among the living beings, for the present period, but that he is the last term of a series beyond which there is no material progress possible upon the plan upon which the whole animal kingdom is constructed, and that the only improvement we may look to upon earth, for the future, must consist in the development of man's intellectual and moral faculties.

The question has been raised of late how far the oldest fossils known may truly be the remains of the first inhabitants of our globe. No doubt extensive tracts of fossiliferous rocks have been intensely altered by plutonic agencies, and their organic contents so entirely destroyed, and the rocks themselves so deeply metamorphosed, that they resemble now more closely eruptive rocks even than stratified deposits. Such changes have taken place again and again up to comparatively recent periods, and upon a very large scale. Yet there are entire continents, North America, for instance, in which the palaeozoic rocks have undergone little, if any, alteration, and where the remains of the earliest representatives of the animal and vegetable kingdoms are as well preserved as in later formations. In such deposits the evidence is satisfactory that a variety of animals belonging to different classes of the great branches of the animal kingdom have existed simultaneously from the beginning; so that the assumption of a successive introduction of these types upon earth is flatly contradicted by well established and well known facts. Moreover, the remains found in the oldest deposits, are everywhere closely allied to one another. In Russia, in Sweden, in Bohemia, and in various other parts of the world, where these oldest formations have been altered upon a more or less extensive scale, as well as in North America, where they have undergone little or no change, they present the same general character, that close correspondence in their structure and in the combination of their families, which shows them to have belonged to contemporaneous faunae. It would, therefore, seem that even where metamorphic rocks prevail, the traces of the earliest inhabitants of this globe have not been entirely obliterated.

SECTION VIII: *The Gradation of Structure Among Animals.*

There is not only variety among animals and plants; they differ also as to their standing, their rank, their superiority or inferiority when compared to one another. But this rank is difficult to determine; for while, in some respects, all animals are equally perfect, as they perform completely the part assigned to them in the general economy of nature, in other respects there are such striking differences between them, that their very agreement in certain features points at their superiority or inferiority in regard to others.

This being the case, the question first arises, Do all animals form one unbroken series from the lowest to the highest? Before the animal kingdom had been studied so closely as it has been of late, many able writers really believed that all animals formed but one simple continuous series, the gradation of which Bonnet has been particularly industrious in trying to ascertain. At a later period, Lamarck has endeavored to show further, that in the complication of their sturcture, all the classes of the animal kingdom represent only successive degrees, and he is so thoroughly convinced that in his systematic arrangement classes constitute one gradual series, that he actually calls the classes "degrees of organization." De Blainville has in the main followed in the steps of Lamarck, though he does not admit quite so simple a series, for he considers the Mollusks and Articulates as two diverging branches ascending from the Radiata, to converge again and unite in the Vertebrata. But since it is now known how the great branches of the animal kingdom may be circumscribed, notwithstanding a few doubtful points, since it is now known how most classes should be characterized, and what is their respective standing; since every day brings dissenting views, respecting the

details of classification, nearer together, the supposition that all
animals constitute one continuous gradated series, can be shown
to be contrary to nature. Yet the greatest difficulty in this inquiry,
is to weigh rightly the respective standing of the four great
branches of the whole animal kingdom; for, however plain the
inferiority of the Radiata may seem, when compared with the
bulk of the Mollusks or Articulata, or still more evident when
contrasted with the Vertebrata, it must not be forgotten, that the
structure of most Echinoderms is far more complicated than
that of any Bryozoon or Ascidian of the type of Mollusks, or that
of any Helminth, of the type of Articulata, and, perhaps, even
superior to that of the *Amphioxus* among Vertebrata. These facts
are so well ascertained, that an absolute superiority or inferiority
of one type over the other must be unconditionally denied. As to
a relative superiority or inferiority however, determined by the
bulk of evidence, though it must be conceded that the Vertebrata
rank above the three other types, the question of the relative
standing of Mollusks and Articulata seems rather to rest upon a
real gradation in their structure; concentration being the prominent trait of the structure of Mollusks, while the expression 'out-
ward display' would more naturally indicate that of Articulata,
and so it might seem as if Mollusks and Articulata were standing
on nearly a level with one another, and as much above Radiata,
as both stand below Vertebrata, but constructed upon plans expressing different tendencies. To appreciate more precisely these
most general relations among the great types of the animal kingdom, will require deeper investigations into the character of their
plan of structure than have been made thus far. Let, however, the
respective standing of these great divisions be what it may; let
them differ only in tendency, or in plan of structure, or in the
height to which they rise, admitting their base to be on one level
or nearly so, so much is certain, that in each type there are representatives exhibiting a highly complicated structure and others
which appear very simple. Now, the very fact that such extremes
may be traced, within the natural boundaries of each type, shows
that in whatever manner these great types are supposed to follow one another in a single series, the highest representative of
the preceding type must join on to the lowest representative of

the following, thus bringing necessarily together the most heterogeneous forms. It must be further evident, that in proportion as the internal arrangement of each great type will be more perfected, the greater is likely to appear the difference at the two ends of the series which are ultimately to be brought into connection with those of other series, in any attempt to establish a single series for all animals.

I doubt whether there is a naturalist now living who could object to an arrangement in which, to determine the respective standing of Radiata, Polyps would be placed lowest, Acalephs next, and Echinoderms highest; a similar arrangement of Mollusks would bring Acephala lowest, Gasteropoda next, and Cephalopoda highest; Articulata would appear in the following order: Worms, Crustacea, and Insects, and Vertebrata, with the Fishes lowest, next Reptiles and Birds, and Mammalia highest. I have here purposely avoided every allusion to controverted points. Now if Mollusks were to follow Radiata in a simple series, Acephala should join on to the Echinoderms; if Articulata, Worms would be the connecting link. We should then have either Cephalopods or Insects, as the highest term of a series beginning with Radiata, followed by Mollusks or by Articulates. In the first case, Cephalopods would be followed by Worms; in the second, Insects by Acephala. Again, the connection with Vertebrata would be made either by Cephalopods, if Articulata were considered as lower than Mollusks, or by Insects, if Mollusks were placed below Articulata. Who does not see, therefore, that in proportion as our knowledge of the true affinities of animals is improving, we accumulate more and more convincing evidence against the idea that the animal kingdom constitutes one simple series?

The next question would then be: Does the animal kingdom constitute several, or any number of graduated series? In attempting to ascertain the value of the less comprehensive groups, when compared to one another, the difficulties seem to be gradually less and less. It is already possible to mark out with tolerable precision, the relative standing between the classes, though even here we do not yet perceive in all the types the same relations. Among Vertebrata, there can be little if any doubt, that the Fishes are lower than the Reptiles, these lower than Birds, and that Mammalia stand highest; it seems equally evident, that in the main, Insects and Crustacea are superior to Worms, Cephalopods to Gasteropods and Acephala and Echinoderms to Acalephs and Polypi. But there are genuine Insects, the superiority of which over many Crustacea, would be difficult to prove; there are Worms which in every respect appear superior to certain Crustacea; the structure of the highest Acephala seems more perfect than that of some Gasteropods, and that of the Halcyonoid Polyps more perfect than that of many Hydroids. Classes do, therefore, not seem to be so limited in the range of their characters, as to justify in every type a complete serial arrangement among them. But when we come to the orders, it can hardly be doubted that the gradation of these natural divisions among themselves in each class, constitutes the very essence of this kind of groups. As a special paragraph is devoted to the consideration of the character of orders in my next chapter, I need not dwell longer upon this point here. It will be sufficient for me to remark now, that the difficulties geologists have met with, in their attempts to compare the rank of the different types of animals and plants with the order of their succession in different geological periods, has chiefly arisen from the circumstance, that they have expected to find a serial gradation, not only among the classes of the same type, where it is only incomplete, but even among the types themselves, between which such a gradation cannot be traced. Had they limited their comparisons to the orders which are really founded upon gradation, the result would have been quite different; but to do this requires more familiarity with Comparative Anatomy, with Embryology and with Zoology proper, than can naturally be expected of those, the studies of which are chiefly devoted to the investigation of the structure of our globe.

To appreciate fully the importance of this question of the gradation of animals, and to comprehend the whole extent of the difficulties involved in it, a superficial acquaintance with the perplexing question of the order of succession of animals in past geological ages, is by no means sufficient; a complete familiarity with the many attempts which have been made to establish a correspondence between the two, and with all the crudities which have been published upon this subject, might dispel every hope to arrive at any satisfactory result upon this subject, did it not appear now, that the inquiry must be circumscribed within different limits, to be conducted upon its true ground. The results to which I have already arrived, since I have perceived the mistake under which investigators have been laboring thus far, in this respect, satisfy me that the point of view under which I have presented the subject here is the true one, and that in the end, the characteristic gradation exhibited by the orders of each class, will present the most striking correspondence with the character of the succession of the same groups in past ages, and afford another startling proof of the admirable order and gradation which have been established from the very beginning, and maintained through all times in the degrees of complication of the structure of animals.

SECTION IX: *Range of Geographical Distribution of Animals.*

The surface of the earth being partly formed by water and partly by land, and the organization of all living beings standing in close relation to the one or the other of these mediums, it is in the nature of things, that no single species, either of animals or plants, should be uniformly distributed over the whole globe. Yet there are some types of the animal, as well as of the vegetable kingdom, which are equably distributed over the whole surface of the land, and others which are as widely scattered in the sea, while others are limited to some continent or some ocean, to some particular province, to some lake, nay, to some very limited spot of the earth's surface.[9]

As far as the primary divisions of animals are concerned, and the nature of the medium to which they are adapted does not interfere, representatives of the four great branches of the animal kingdom are everywhere found together. Radiata, Mollusks, Articulata, and Vertebrata occur together in every part of the ocean, in the Arctics, as well as under the equator, and near the

southern pole as far as man has penetrated; every bay, every in-
let, every shoal is haunted by them. So universal is this association, not only at present but in all past geological ages, that I consider it as a sufficient reason to expect, that fishes will be found in
those few fossiliferous beds of the Silurian System, in which thus
far they have not yet been found. Upon land, we find equally
everywhere Vertebrata, Articulata, and Mollusks, but no Radiata,
this whole branch being limited to the waters; but as far as terrestrial animals extend, we find representatives of the other three
branches associated, as we find them all four in the sea. Classes
have already a more limited range of distribution. Among Radiata, the Polypi, Acalephs, and Echinoderms are not only aquatic,
they are all marine, with a single exception, the genus Hydra,
which inhabits fresh waters. Among Mollusks, the Acephala are
all aquatic, but partly marine and partly fluviatile, the Gasteropoda partly marine, partly fluviatile and partly terrestrial, while
all Cephalopoda are marine. Among Articulata, the Worms are
partly marine, partly fluviatile, and partly terrestrial, while many
are internal parasites, living in the cavities or in the organs of
other animals; the Crustacea are partly marine and partly fluviatile, a few are terrestrial; the Insects are mostly terrestrial
or rather aerial, yet some are marine, other fluviatile, and a
large number of those, which in their perfect state live in the
air, are terrestrial or even aquatic during their earlier stages
of growth. Among Vertebrata the Fishes are all aquatic, but
partly marine and partly fluviatile; the Reptiles are either aquatic,
or amphibious or terrestrial, and some of the latter are aquatic
during the early part of their life; the Birds are all aerial, but
some more terrestrial and others more aquatic; finally, the Mammalia though all aerial live partly in the sea, partly in fresh water,
but mostly upon land. A more special review might show, that
this localization in connection with the elements in which animals
live, has a direct reference on peculiarities of structure of such
importance, that a close consideration of the habitat of animals
within the limits of the classes, might in most cases lead to a very
natural classification. But this is true only within the limits of the
classes, and even here not absolutely, as in some the orders only,
or the families only are thus closely related to the elements; there

are even natural groups, in which this connection is not manifested beyond the limits of the genera, and a few cases in which it is actually confined to the species. Yet, in every degree of these connections, we find that upon every spot of the globe, it extends simultaneously to the representatives of different classes and even of different branches of the animal and vegetable kingdoms; a circumstance which shows that when called into existence, in such an association, these various animals and plants were respectively adapted with all the peculiarities of their kingdom, those of their class, those of their order, those of their genus, and those of their species, to the home assigned to them, and therefore, not produced by the nature of the place, or of the element, or any other physical condition. To maintain the contrary, would really amount to asserting that wherever a variety of organized beings live together, no matter how great their diversity, the physical agents prevailing there, must have in their combined action, the power of producing such a diversity of structures as exists in animals, notwithstanding the close connection in which these animals stand to them, or to work out an intimate relation to themselves in beings, the essential characteristics of which, have no reference to their nature. In other words, in all these animals and plants, there is one side of their organization which has an immediate reference to the elements in which they live, and another which has no such connection, and yet it is precisely this part of the structure of animals and plants, which has no direct bearing upon the conditions in which they are placed in nature, which constitutes their essential, their typical character. This proves beyond the possibility of an objection, that the element in which animals and plants live (and under this expression I mean to include all that is commonly called physical agents, physical causes, etc.) cannot in any way be considered as the cause of their existence.

If the naturalists of past centuries have failed to improve their systems of Zoology by introducing considerations derived from the habitat of animals, it is chiefly because they have taken this habitat as the foundation of their primary divisions; but reduced to its proper limits, the study of the connection between the structure and the natural home of animals cannot fail to lead to interesting results, among which, the growing conviction that these relations are not produced by physical agents, but determined in the plan ordained from the beginning, will not be the least important.

The unequal limitation of groups of a different value, upon the surface of the earth, produces the most diversified combination possible, when we consider the mode of association of different families of animals and plants in different parts of the world. These combinations are so regulated that every natural province has a character of its own, as far as its animals and plants are concerned, and such natural associations of organized beings extending over a wider or narrower area are called *Faunae* when the animals alone are considered, and *Florae* when the plants alone are regarded. Their natural limits are far from being yet ascertained satisfactorily everywhere. As the works of Schow and Schmarda may suffice to give an approximate idea of their extent, I would refer to them for further details, and allude here only to the unequal extent of these different faunae, and to the necessity of limiting them in different ways, according to the point of view under which they are considered, or rather show that, as different groups have a wider or more limited range, in investigating their associations, or the faunae, we must distinguish between zoological realms, zoological provinces, zoological counties, zoological fields, as it were; that is, between zoological areas of unequal value over the widest of which range the most extensive types, while in their smaller and smaller divisions, we find more and more limited types, sometimes overlapping one another, sometimes placed side by side, sometimes concentric to one another, but always and everywhere impressing a special character upon some part of a wider area, which is thus made to differ from that of any other part within its natural limits.

These various combinations of smaller or wider areas, equally well defined in different types, have given rise to the conflicting views prevailing among naturalists respecting the natural limits of faunae; but with the progress of our knowledge these discrepancies cannot fail to disappear. In some respect, every island of the Pacific upon which distinct animals are found, may be considered as exhibiting a distinct fauna, yet several groups of these islands have a common character, which unites them into more comprehensive faunae, the Sandwich Islands for instance, compared to the Fejees or to New Zealand. What is true of disconnected islands or of isolated lakes is equally true of connected parts of the mainland and of the ocean.

Since it is well known that many animals are limited to a very narrow range in their geographical distribution, it would be a highly interesting subject of inquiry to ascertain what are the narrowest limits within which animals of different types may be circumscribed, as this would furnish the first basis for a scientific consideration of the conditions under which animals may have been created. The time is passed when the mere indication of the continent whence an animal had been obtained, could satisfy our curiosity; and the naturalists who, having an opportunity of ascertaining closely the particular circumstances under which the animals they describe are placed in their natural home, are guilty of a gross disregard of the interest of science when they neglect to relate them. Our knowledge of the geographical distribution of animals would be far more extensive and precise than it is now, but for this neglect; every new fact relating to the geographical distribution of well-known species is as important to science as the discovery of a new species. Could we only know the range of a single animal as accurately as Alphonse De Candolle has lately determined that of many species of plants, we might begin a new era in Zoology. It is greatly to be regretted that in most works, containing the scientific results of explorations of distant countries, only new species are described, when the mere enumeration of those already known might have added invaluable information respecting their geographical distribution. The carelessness with which some naturalists distinguish species merely because they are found in distant regions, without even attempting to secure specimens for comparison, is a perpetual source of erroneous conclusions in the study of the geographical distribution of organized beings, not less determined to the progress of science than the readiness of others to consider as identical, animals and plants which may resemble each other closely, without paying the least regard to their distinct origin, and without even pointing out the differences they may perceive between specimens from different parts of the world. The perfect identity of animals and plants living in very remote parts of the globe has so often been ascertained, and it is also so well known how closely species may be allied and yet differ in all the essential relations which characterize species, that such loose investigations are no longer justifiable.

This close resemblance of animals and plants in distant parts of the world is the most interesting subject of investigation with reference to the question of the unity of origin of animals, and to that of the influence of physical agents upon organized beings in general. It appears to me that as the facts point now distinctly to an independent origin of individuals of the same species in remote regions, or of closely allied species representing one another in distant parts of the world, one of the strongest arguments in favor of the supposition that physical agents may have had a controlling influence in changing the character of the organic world, is gone for ever.

The narrowest limits within which certain Vertebrata may be circumscribed, is exemplified, among Mammalia, by some large and remarkable species: the Orang-Outangs upon the Sunda Islands, the Chimpanzee and the Gorilla along the western coast of Africa, several distinct species of Rhinoceros about the Cape of Good Hope, and in Java and Sumatra, the Pinchaque and the common Tapir in South America, and the eastern Tapir in Sumatra, the East Indian and the African Elephant, the Bactrian Camel and the Dromedary, the Llamas, and the different kinds of wild Bulls, wild Goats, and wild Sheep, etc.; among birds by the African Ostrich, the two American Rheas, the Casovary (*Dromicejus*) of New Holland, and the Emeu (*Casuarius galeatus*) of the Indian Archipelago, and still more by the different species of doves confined to particular islands in the Pacific Ocean; among Reptiles, by the *Proteus* of the cave of Adelsberg in Carinthia, by the Gopher (*Testudo Polyphemus* Auct.) of our Southern States; among fishes, by the Blind Fish (*Amblyopsis spelaeus*) of the Mammoth Cave. Examples of closely limited Articulata may not be so striking, yet the Blind Crawfish of the Mammoth Cave and the many parasites found only upon or within certain species of animals, are very remarkable in this respect. Among Mollusks, I would remark the many species of land shells, ascertained by Professor Adams to occur only in Jamaica, among the West India Islands, and the species discovered by the United States Exploring Expedition upon isolated islands of the Pacific, and described by Dr. Gould. Even among Radiata many species might be quoted, among Echinoderms as well as among Medusae and Polypi, which are only known from a few localities; but as long as these animals are not collected with the special view of ascertaining their geographical range, the indications of travellers must be received with great caution, and any generalization respecting the extent of their natural area would be premature as long as the countries they inhabit have not been more extensively explored. It is nevertheless true as established by ample evidence, that within definite limits all the animals occurring in different natural zoological provinces are specifically distinct. What remains to be ascertained more minutely is the precise range of each species, as well as the most natural limits of the different faunae.

SECTION X: *Identity of Structure of Widely Distributed Types.*

It is not only when considering the diversification of the animal kingdom within limited geographical areas, that we are called upon in our investigations to admire the unity of plan its most diversified types may exhibit; the identity of structure of these types is far more surprising, when we trace it over a wide range of country, and within entirely disconnected areas. Why the animals and plants of North America should present such a strong resemblance to those of Europe and Northern Asia, while those of Australia are so entirely different from those of Africa and South America under the same latitudes, is certainly a problem of great interest in connection with the study of the influence of physical agents upon the character of animals and plants in different parts of the world. North America certainly does not resemble Europe and Northern Asia, more than parts of Australia resemble certain parts of Africa or of South America, and even if a greater difference should be conceded between the latter than between the former, these disparities are in no way commensurate with the difference or similarity of their organized beings, nor in any way rationally dependent one upon the other. Why should the identity of species prevailing in the Arctics not extend to the temperate zone, when many species of this zone, though different, are as difficult to distinguish, as it is difficult to prove the identity of certain arctic species, in the different continents converging to the north, and when besides, those of the two zones mingle to a great extent at their boundaries? Why are the antarctic species not identical with those of the arctic regions? And why should a further increase of the average temperature introduce such completely new types, when even in the Arctics, there are in different continents such strikingly peculiar types (the *Rhytina* for instance) combined with those that are identical over the whole arctic area? [10]

It may at first sight seem very natural that the arctic species should extend over the three northern continents converging towards the north pole, as there can be no insuperable barrier to the widest dissemination over this whole area for animals living in a glacial ocean or upon parts of three continents which are almost bound together by ice. Yet the more we trace this identity in detail, the more surprising does it appear, as we find in the Arctics as well as everywhere else, representatives of different types living together. The arctic Mammalia belonging chiefly to the families of Whales, Seals, Bears, Weasels, Foxes, Ruminants and Rodents, have, as Mammalia, the same general structure as the Mammalia of any other part of the globe, and so have the arctic Birds, the arctic Fishes, the arctic Articulata, the arctic Mollusks, the arctic Radiata when compared to the representatives of the same types all over our globe. This identity extends to every degree of affinity among these animals and the plants which accompany them; their orders, their families, and their genera as far as they have representatives elsewhere, bear everywhere the same identical ordinal, family, or generic characters; the arctic foxes have the same dental formula, the same toes and claws, in fact, every generic peculiarity which characterizes foxes, whether they live in the Arctics, or in the temperate or tropical zone, in America, in Europe, in Africa, or in Asia. This is equally true of the seals or the whales; the same details of structure which characterize their genera in the Arctics reappear in the Antarctics, and the intervening space, as far as their natural distribution goes. This is equally true of the birds, the fishes, etc., etc. And let it not be supposed that it is only a general resemblance. By no means. The structural identity extends to the most minute details in the most intimate structure of the teeth, of the hair, of the scales, in the furrows of the brain, in the ramification of the vessels, in the folds of the internal surface of the intestine, in the complication of the glands, etc., etc., to peculiarities, indeed, which nobody but a professional naturalist conversant with microscopic anatomy, would ever believe could present such precise and permanent characters. So complete, indeed, is this identity, that were any of these beings submitted to the investigation of a skilful anatomist, after having been mutilated to such an extent that none of its specific characters could be recognized, yet not only its class, or its order, or its family, but even its genus, could be identified as precisely as if it were perfectly well preserved in all its parts. Were the genera few which have a wide range upon the earth and in the ocean, this might be considered as an extraordinary case; but there is no class of animals and plants which does not contain many genera, more or less cosmopolite in their geographical distribution. The number of animals which have a wide distribution is even so great that, as far at least as genera are concerned, it may fairly be said, that the majority of them have an extensive geographical range. This amounts to the most complete evidence that, as far as any of these genera extends in its geographical distribution, animals the structure of which is identical within this range of distribution, are entirely beyond the influence of physical agents, unless these agents have the power, notwithstanding their extreme diversity, within these very same geographical limits, to produce absolutely identical structures of the most diversified types.

It must be remembered here, that there are genera of Vertebrata, of Articulata, of Mollusks, and of Radiata, which occupy the same identical and wide geographical distribution and that while the structure of their respective representatives is identical over the whole area, as Vertebrata, as Articulata, as Mollusks, as Radiata, they are at the same time built upon the most different plans. I hold this fact to be in itself a complete demonstration of the entire independence of physical agents of the structure of animals, and I may add that the vegetable kingdom presents a series of facts identical with these. This proves that all the higher relations among animals and plants are determined by other causes than mere physical influences.

While all the representatives of the same genus are identical in structure, the different species of one genus differ only in their size, in the proportions of their parts, in their ornamentation, in their relations to the surrounding elements, etc. The geographical range of these species varies so greatly, that it cannot afford in itself a criterion for the distinction of species. It appears further, that while some species which are scattered over very extensive areas, occupy disconnected parts of that area, other species closely allied to one another and which are generally designated under the name of representative species, occupy respectively such disconnected sections of these areas. The question then arises, how these natural boundaries assigned to every species are established. It is now generally believed that each species had, in the beginning, some starting point, from which it has spread over the whole range of the area it now occupies, and that this starting point is still indicated by the prevalence or concentration of such species in some particular part of its natural area, which, on that account, is called its centre of distribution or centre of creation, while at its external limits the representatives of such species thin out, as it were, occurring more sparsely and sometimes in a reduced condition.

It was a great progress in our science, when the more extensive and precise knowledge of the geographical distribution of organized beings forced upon its cultivators the conviction, that neither animals nor plants could have originated upon one and the same spot upon the surface of the earth, and hence have spread more and more widely until the whole globe became inhabited. It was really an immense progress which freed science

from the fetters of an old prejudice; for now we have the facts
of the case before us, it is really difficult to conceive how, by assuming such a gradual dissemination from one spot, the diversity
which exists in every part of the globe could ever have seemed to
be explained. But even to grant distinct centres of distribution
for each species within their natural boundaries, is only to meet
the facts half way, as there are innumerable relations between
the animals and plants which we find associated everywhere,
which must be considered as primitive, and cannot be the result
of successive adaptation. And if this be so, it would follow that
all animals and plants have occupied, from the beginning, those
natural boundaries within which they stand to one another in
such harmonious relations. Pines have originated in forests, heaths
in heathers, grasses in prairies, bees in hives, herrings in schools,
buffaloes in herds, men in nations! I see a striking proof that this
must have been the case in the circumstance, that representative
species, which, as distinct species, must have had from the beginning a different and distinct geographical range, frequently occupy sections of areas which are simultaneously inhabited by the
representatives of other species, which are perfectly identical
over the whole area. By way of an example, I would mention the
European and the American Widgeon (*Anas 'Mareca' Penelope*
and *A. americana*), or the American and the European Red-
headed Ducks (*A. ferina* and *A. erythrocephala*), which inhabit
respectively the northern parts of the Old and New World in
summer, and migrate further south in these same continents during winter, while the Mallard (*A. Boschas*) and the Scaup Duck
(*A. marila*) are as common in North America as in Europe. What
do these facts tell: That all these birds originated together somewhere, where they no longer occur, to establish themselves in the
end within the limits they now occupy?—or that they originated
either in Europe or America, where, it is true, they do not live all
together, but at least a part of them?—or that they really originated within the natural boundaries they occupy? I suppose with
sensible readers I need only argue the conclusions flowing from
the last supposition. If so, the American Widgeon and the American Red-headed Duck originated in America, and the European
Widgeon and the European Red-headed Duck in Europe. But

what of the Mallard and the Scaup, which are equally common upon the two continents; did they first appear in Europe, or in America, or simultaneously upon the two continents? Without entering into further details, as I have only desired to lay clearly a distinct case before my readers, from which the character of the argument, which applies to the whole animal kingdom, may be fully understood, I say that the facts lead, step by step, to the inference, that such birds as the Mallard and the Scaup originated simultaneously and separately in Europe and in America, and that all animals originated in vast numbers, indeed, in the average number characteristic of their species, over the whole of their geographical area, whether its surface be continuous or disconnected by sea, lakes, or rivers, or by differences of level above the sea, etc. The details of the geographical distribution of animals exhibit, indeed, too much discrimination to admit for a moment that it could be the result of accident, that is, the result of the accidental migrations of the animals or of the accidental dispersion of the seeds of plants. The greater the uniformity of structure of these widely distributed organized beings, the less probable does their accidental distribution appear. I confess that nothing has ever surprised me so much as to see the perfect identity of the most delicate microscopic structures of animals and plants, from the remotest parts of the world. It was this striking identity of structure in the same types, this total independence of the essential characteristics of animals and plants, of their distribution under the most extreme climatic differences known upon our globe, which led me to distrust the belief, then almost universal, that organized beings are influenced by physical causes to a degree which may essentially modify their character.

SECTION XI: *Community of Structure Among Animals Living in the Same Regions.*

The most interesting result of the earliest investigations of the fauna of Australia was the discovery of a type of animals, the

Marsupialia, prevailing upon this continental island, which are unknown in almost every other part of the world. Every student of Natural History knows now that there are no *Quadrumana* in New Holland, neither Monkeys, nor Makis: no *Insectivora,* neither Shrews, nor Moles, nor Hedgehogs; no true *Carnivora,* neither Bears, nor Weasels, nor Foxes, nor Viverras, nor Hyenas, nor Wild Cats; no *Edentata,* neither Sloths, nor Tatous, nor Ant-eaters, nor Pangolins; no *Pachyderms,* neither Elephants, nor Hippopotamuses, nor Hogs, nor Rhinoceroses, nor Tapirs, nor Wild Horses; no *Ruminantia,* neither Camels, nor Llamas, nor Deers, nor Goats, nor Sheep, nor Bulls, etc., and yet the Mammalia of Australia are almost as diversified as those of any other continent. In the words of Waterhouse, who has studied them with particular care, "the Marsupialia present a remarkable diversity of structure, containing herbivorous, carnivorous, and insectivorous species; indeed, we find amongst the marsupial animals analogous representations of most of the other order of Mammalia. The *Quadrumana* are represented by the Phelangers, the *Carnivora* by the Dasyuri, the *Insectivora* by the small Phascogales, the *Ruminantia* by the Kangaroos, and the *Edentata* by the Monotremes. The Cheiroptera are not represented by any known marsupial animals, and the Rodents are represented by a single species only; the hiatus is filled up, however, in both cases, by placental species, for Bats and Rodents are tolerably numerous in Australia, and, if we except the Dog, which it is probable has been introduced by man, these are the only placental Mammalia found in that continent." Nevertheless, all these animals have in common some most striking anatomical characters, which distinguish them from all other Mammalia, and stamp them as one of the most natural groups of that class; their mode of reproduction, and the connection of the young with the mother, are different; so, also, is the structure of their brain, etc.

Now, the suggestion that such peculiarities could be produced by physical agents is for ever set aside by the fact that neither the birds nor the reptiles, nor, indeed, any other animals of New Holland, depart in such a manner from the ordinary character of their representatives in other parts of the world; unless it could be shown that such agents have the power of discrimination, and may produce, under the same conditions, beings which agree and others which do not agree with those of different continents; not to speak again of the simultaneous occurrence in that same continent of other heterogeneous types of Mammalia, Bats and Rodents, which occur there as well as everywhere else in other continents. Nor is New Holland the only part of the world which nourishes animals highly diversified among themselves, and yet presenting common characters strikingly different from those of the other members of their type, circumscribed within definite geographical areas. Almost every part of the globe exhibits some such group either of animals or of plants, and every class of organized beings contains some native natural group, more or less extensive, more or less prominent, which is circumscribed within peculiar geographical limits. Among Mammalia we might quote further the Quadrumana, the representatives of which, though greatly diversified in the Old as well as in the New World, differ and agree respectively in many important points of their structure; also the Edentata of South America.

Among birds, the Humming Birds, which constitute a very natural, beautiful, and numerous family, all of which are nevertheless confined to America only, as the Pheasants are to the Old World Among Reptiles, the Crocodiles of the Old World compared to those of America. Among fishes, the family of *Labyrinthici*, which is confined to the Indian and Pacific Oceans, that of Goniodonts, which is limited to the fresh waters of South America, as that of Cestraciontes to the Pacific. The comparative anatomy of Insects is not sufficiently far advanced to furnish striking examples of this kind; among Insects, however, remarkable for their form, which are limited to particular regions, may be quoted the genus *Mormolyce* of Java, the *Pneumora* of the Cape of Good Hope, the *Belostoma* of North America, the *Fulgora* of China, etc. The geological distribution of Crustacea has been treated in such a masterly manner by Dana, in his great work upon the Crustacea of the United States Exploring Expedition, Vol. XIII., p. 1451, that I can only refer to it for numerous examples of localized types of this class, and also as a model how to deal with such subjects. Among Worms, the *Peripates* of Guiana deserves to be mentioned. Among Cephalopods, the *Nautilus* in Amboyna. Among Gasteropods, the genus *Io* in the western waters of the United States. Among Acephala, the *Trigonia* in New Holland, certain Naiades in the United States, the *Aetheria* in the Nile. Among Echinoderms, the *Pentacrinus* in the West Indies, the *Culcita* in Zanzibar, the *Amblypneustes* in the Pacific, the *Temnopleurus* in the Indian Ocean, the Dendraster' on the western coast of North America. Among Acalephs, the *Berenice* of New Holland. Among Polypi, the true *Fungidae* in the Indian and Pacific Oceans, the *Renilla* in the Atlantic, etc.

Many more examples might be quoted, were our knowledge of the geographical distribution of the lower animals more precise. But these will suffice to show that whether high or low, aquatic or terrestrial, there are types of animals remarkable for their peculiar structure which are circumscribed within definite limits, and this localization of special structures is a striking confirmation of the view expressed already in another connection, that the organization of animals, whatever it is, may be adapted to various and identical conditions of existence, and can in no way be considered as originating from these conditions.

SECTION XII: *Serial Connection in the Structure of Animals Widely Scattered upon the Surface of Our Globe.*

Ever since I have become acquainted with the reptiles inhabiting different parts of the world, I have been struck with a remarkable fact, not yet noticed by naturalists, as far as I know, and of which no other class exhibits such striking examples. This fact is that among Saurians, as well as among Betrachians, there are families, the representatives of which, though scattered all over the globe, form the most natural connected series, in which every link represents one particular degree of development. The Scinoids, among Saurians, are one of these families. It contains about one hundred species, referred by Dumeril and Bibron to thirty-one genera, which, in the development of their organs of locomotion, exhibit most remarkable combinations, illustrated in a diagram, on the following pages.

Fully to appreciate the meaning of this diagram, it ought to be remembered, that the animals belonging to this family are considered here in two different points of view. In the first place, their zoological relations to one another are expressed by the various combinations of the structure of their legs; some having four legs, and these are the most numerous, others only two legs, which are always the hind legs, and others still no legs at all. Again these legs may have only one toe, or two, three, four, or five toes, and the number of toes may vary between the fore and hind legs. The classification adopted here is based upon these characters. In the second place, the geographical distribution is noticed. But it is at once apparent that the home of these animals stands in no relation whatsoever to their zoological arrangement. On the contrary, the most remote genera may occur in the same country, while the most closely related may live far apart.

GENERA WITH FOUR LEGS

Tropidophorus, 1 species, Cochin-China.
Scincus, 1 sp., Syria, North and West Africa.
Sphenops, 1 sp., Egypt.
Diploglossus, 6 sp., West Indies and Brazils.
Amphiglossus, 1 sp., Madagascar.
Gongylus, with 7 sub-genera:

Gongylus, 2 sp., Southern Europe, Egypt, Teneriffe, Isle de France.

Eumeces, 11 sp., East and West Indies, South America, Vanikora, New Ireland, New Guinea, Pacific Islands.

With *five* toes to the fore feet, as well as to the hind feet:

Euprepes, 13 sp., West coast of Africa, Cape of Good Hope, Egypt, Abyssinia, Seychelles, Madagascar, New Guinea, East Indies, Sunda Islands, Manila.

Plestiodon, 5 sp., Egypt, Algiers, China, Japan, United States.

Lygosoma, 19 sp., New Holland, New Zealand, Java, New Guinea, Timor, East Indies, Pacific Islands, United States.

Leiolopisma, 1 sp., Mauritius and Manila.
Tropidolopisma, 1 sp., New Holland.
Cyclodus, 3 sp., New Holland and Java.
Trachysaurus, 1 sp., New Holland.
Ablepharus, 4 sp., Southeastern Europe, New Holland, Pacific Islands.

With *five* toes to the fore feet and *four* toes to the hind feet: *Campsodactylus*, 1 sp., Bengal.

With *four* toes to the fore feet and *five* toes to the hind feet:
{ *Heteropus*, 3 sp., Africa, New Holland, Isle de France.
Gymnophthalmus, 1 sp., W. Indies and Brazil.

With *four* toes to the fore feet and *four* toes to the hind feet:
{ *Tetradactylus*, 1 sp., New Holland. The genus Chalcides of the allied family Chalcidioids, exhibits another example of this combination.

With *four* toes to the fore feet and *three* toes to the hind feet: No examples known of this combination.

With *three* toes to the fore feet and *four* toes to the hind feet: Not known.

With *three* toes to the fore feet and *three* toes to the hind feet:
{ *Hemiergis*, 1 sp., New Holland.
Seps, 1 sp., S. Europe and N. Africa.
Nessia, 1 sp., Origin unknown.

With *three* toes to the fore feet and *two* toes to the hind feet: Not known.

With *two* toes to the fore feet and *three* toes to the hind feet:
{ *Heteromeles*, 1 sp., Algiers.
Lerista, 1 sp., New Holland.

With *two* toes to the fore feet and *two* toes to the hind feet: *Chelomeles*, 1 sp., New Holland.

With *two* toes to the fore feet and *one* toe to the hind feet: *Brachymeles*, 1 sp., Philippine Islands.

With *one* toe to the fore feet and *two* toes to the hind feet: *Brachystopus*, 1 sp., South Africa.

With *one* toe to the fore feet and *one* toe to the hind feet: *Evesia*, 1 sp., Origin unknown.

GENERA WITH ONLY TWO LEGS

No representatives are known *with fore legs only;* but this structural combination occurs in the allied family of the Chalcidioids. The representatives *with hind legs only,* present the following combinations:—

With *two* toes: *Scelotes,* 1 sp., Cape Good Hope.
With *one* toe: *Propeditus,* 1 sp., Cape Good Hope and New Holland.
Ophiodes, 1 sp., South America.
Hysteropus, 1 sp., New Holland.
Lialis, 1 sp., New Holland.
Dibamus, 1 sp., New Guinea.

GENERA WITHOUT ANY LEGS

Anguis, 1 sp., Europe, Western Asia, Northern Africa.
Ophiomorus, 1 sp., Morea, Southern Russia, and Algiers.
Acontias, 1 sp., Southern Africa, Cape Good Hope.
Typhlina, 1 sp., Southern Africa, Cape Good Hope.

Who can look at this diagram, and not recognize in its arrangement the combinations of thought? This is so obvious, that while considering it one might almost overlook the fact, that while it was drawn up to classify animals preserved in the Museum of the Jardin des Plantes in Paris, it is in reality inscribed in Nature by these animals themselves, and is only read off when they are brought together, and compared side by side. But it contains an important element for our discussion: the series is not built up of equivalent representatives in its different terms, some combinations being richly endowed, others numbering a few, or even a single genus, and still others being altogether disregarded; such freedom indicates selection, and not the working of the law of necessity.

And if from a contemplation of this remarkable series we turn our attention to the indications relating to the geographical distribution of these so closely linked genera, inscribed after their names, we perceive at once, that they are scattered all over the globe, but not so that there could be any connection between the combinations of their structural characters and their homes. The types without legs are found in Europe, in Western Asia, in Northern Africa, and at the Cape of Good Hope; the types with hind legs only, and with one single toe, at the Cape of Good Hope, in South America, New Holland, and New Guinea; those with two toes at the Cape of Good Hope only. Among the types with four legs the origin of those with but one toe to each foot is unknown, those with one toe in the fore foot and two in the hind foot occur in the Philippine Islands, those with two toes to all four feet in New Holland, those with three toes to the hind feet and two to the fore feet in Algiers and New Holland; none are known with three toes to the fore feet and two to the hind feet. Those with three toes to the four feet inhabit Europe, Northern Africa, and New Holland. There are none with three and four toes, either in the fore feet or in the hind feet. Those with four toes to the four feet live in New Holland; those with five toes to the fore feet and four to the hind feet, in Bengal, and with four toes in the fore feet and five in the hind feet, in Africa, the West Indies, the Brazils, and New Holland. Those with five toes to all four feet have the widest distribution, and yet they are so scattered that no single zoological province presents any thing like a complete series; on the contrary, the mixture of some of the representatives with perfect feet with others which have them rudimentary, in almost every fauna, excludes still more decidedly the idea of an influence of physical agents upon this development.

Another similar series, not less striking, may be traced among the Batrachians, for the characters of which I may refer to the works of Holbrook, Tschudi, and Baird, even though they have not presented them in this connection, as the characteristics of the genera will of themselves suggest their order, and further details upon this subject would be superfluous for my purpose, the more so, as I have already discussed the gradation of these animals elsewhere.

Similar series, though less conspicuous and more limited, may be traced in every class of the animal kingdom, not only among the living types, but also among the representatives of past geological ages, which adds to the interest of such series in showing, that the combinations include not only the element of space, indicating omnipresence, but also that of time, which involves prescience. The series of Crinoids, that of Brachiopods through all geological ages, that of the Nautiloids, that of Ammonitoids from the Trias to the Cretaceous formation inclusive, that of Trilobites from the lowest beds up to the Carboniferous period, that of Ganoids through all formations; then again among living animals in the class of Mammalia, the series of Monkeys in the Old World especially, that of Carnivora from the Seals, through the Plantigrades, to the Digitigrades; in the class of Birds, that of the Wading Birds, and that of the Gallinaceous Birds; in the class of Fishes, that of Pleuronectidae and Gadoids, that of Skates and Sharks; in the class of Insects, that of Lepidoptera from the Tineina to the Papilionina; in the class of Crustacea, that of the Decapods in particular; in the class of Worms, that of the Nudibranchiata or that of the Dorsibranchiata especially; in the class of Cephalopoda, that of the Sepioids; in the class of Gasteropoda, that of the Nudibranchiata in particular; in the class of Acephala, that of the Ascidians and that of the Oysters in the widest sense; in the class of Echinoderms, those of Holothuriae and Asterioids; in the class of Acalephs, that of the Hydroids; in the class of Polyps, that of the Halcynoids, of the Atraeoids, etc., etc., deserve particular attention, and may be studied with great advantage in reference to the points under consideration. For everywhere do we observe in them, with reference to space and to time, the thoughtful combinations of an active mind. But it ought not to be overlooked, that while some types represent strikingly connected series, there are others in which nothing of the kind seems to exist, and the diversity of which involves other considerations.

SECTION XIII: *Relation Between the Size of Animals, and Their Structure.*

The relation between the size and structure of animals has been very little investigated, though even the most superficial survey of the animal kingdom may satisfy any one, that there is a decided relation between size and structure among them. Not that I mean to assert that size and structure form parallel series, or that all animals of one branch, or even those of the same class or the same order, agree very closely with one another in reference to size. This element of their organization is not defined within those limits, though the Vertebrata, as a whole, are larger than either Articulata, Mollusks, or Radiata; though Mammalia are larger than Birds, Crustacea larger than Insects; though Cetacea are larger than Herbivora, these larger than Carnivora, etc. The true limit at which, in the organization of animals, size acquires a real importance, is that of families, that is, the groups which are essentially distinguished by their form, as if form and size were correlative as far as the structure of animals is concerned. The representatives of natural families are indeed closely similar in that respect; the extreme differences are hardly anywhere tenfold within these limits, and frequently only double. A few examples, selected among the most natural families, will show this. Omitting mankind, on account of the objections which might be made against the idea that it embraces any original diversity, let us consider the different families of Monkeys, of Bats, of Insectivora, of Carnivora, of Rodents, of Pachyderms, of Ruminants, etc., among Birds, the Vultures, the Eagles, the Falcons, the Owls, the Swallows, the Finches, the Warblers, the Humming Birds, the Doves, the Wrens, the Ostriches, the Herons, the Plovers, the Gulls, the Ducks, the Pelicans; among Reptiles, the Crocodiles, the different families of Chelonians, of Lizards, of Snakes, the Frogs proper, the Toads, etc.; among Fishes, the Sharks and Skates, the Herrings, the Codfishes, the Cyprinnodonts, the Chaetodonts, the Lophobranchii, the Ostracionts, etc.; among Insects, the Sphingoidae or the Tineina, the Longicorns or the Coccinellina, the Bomboidae or the Brachonidae; among Crustacea, the Cancroidea or the Pinnotheroidae, the Limuloidae or the Cypridoidae, and the Rotifera; among Worms, the Dorsibranchiata or the Naioidae; among Mollusks, the Stromboidae or the Buccinoidae, the Helicinoidae or the Limnaeoidae, the Chamacea or the Cycladoidae; among Radiata, the Asterioidae and the Ophiuroidae, the Hydroids and the Discophorae, the Astraeoidae and the Actinioidae.

Having thus recalled some facts which go to show what are the limits within which size and structure are more directly connected,[11] it is natural to infer, that since size is such an important character of species, and extends distinctly its cycle of relationship to the families or even further, it can as little be supposed to be determined by physical agents as the structure itself with which it is so closely connected, both bearing similar relations to these agents.

Life is regulated by a quantitative element in the structure of all organized beings, which is as fixed and as precisely determined as every other feature depending more upon the quality of the organs or their parts. This shows the more distinctly the presence of a specific, immaterial principle in each kind of animals and plants, as all begin their existence in the condition of ovules of a microscopic size, exhibiting in all a wonderful similarity of structure. And yet these primitive ovules, so identical at first in their physical consitution, never produce any thing different from the parents; all reach respectively, through a succession of unvarying changes, the same final result, the reproduction of a new being identical with the parents. How does it then happen, that, if physical agents have such a powerful influence in shaping the character of organized beings, we see no trace of it in the innumerable instances in which these ovules are discharged in the elements in which they undergo their further development, at a period when the germ they contain, has not yet assumed any of those more determined characteristics which distinguish the full-grown animal or the perfect plant? Do physicists know of a law of the material world which presents any such analogy to these phenomena, that it could be considered as accounting for them?

In this connection it should be further remembered, that these cycles of size characteristic of different families, are entirely different for animals of different types, though living together under identical circumstances.

SECTION XIV: *Relations Between the Size of Animals, and the Mediums in Which They Live.*

It has just been remarked, that animals of different types, even when living together, are framed in structures of different size. Yet, life is so closely combined with the elements of nature, that each type shows decided relations, within its own limits, to these elements as far as size is concerned. The aquatic Mammalia, as a whole, are larger than the terrestrial ones; so are the aquatic Birds, and the aquatic Reptiles. In families which are essentially terrestrial, the species which take to the water are generally larger than those which remain permanently in water. The same relation is observed in the different families of Insects which number aquatic and terrestrial species. It is further remarkable, that among aquatic animals, the fresh-water types are inferior in size to the marine ones; the marine Turtles are all larger than the largest inhabitants of our rivers and ponds, the more aquatic Trionyx larger than the Emyds and among these the more aquatic Chelydra larger than the true Emys, and these generally larger than the more terrestrial Clemmys or the Cistudo. The class of Fishes has its largest representatives in the sea; fresh-water fishes are on the whole dwarfs, in comparison to their marine relatives, and the largest of them, our Sturgeons and Salmons, go to the sea. The same relations obtain among Crustacea; to be satisfied of the fact, we need only compare our Crawfishes with the Lobsters, our Apus with Limulus, etc. Among Worms, the Earthworms and Leeches furnish a still wider range of comparisons when contrasted with the marine types. Among Gasteropods and Acephala, this obtains to the same extent; the most gigantic Ampullariae and Anodontae are small in comparison to certain Fusus, Voluta, Tritonium, Cassis, Strombus, or to the Tridacna. Among Radiata even, which are all marine, with the exception of the single genus Hydra, this rule holds good, as the fresh water Hydroids are among the smallest Acalephs known.

This coincidence, upon such an extensive scale, seems to be most favorable to the view that animals are modified by the immediate influence of the elements; yet I consider it as affording one of the most striking proofs that there is no causal connection between them. Were it otherwise, the terrestrial and the aquatic representatives of the same family could not be so similar as they are in all their essential characteristics, which actually stand in no relation whatsoever to these elements. What constitutes the Bear in the Polar Bear, is not its adaptation to an aquatic mode of existence. What makes the Whales Mammalia, bears no relation to the sea. What constitutes Earthworms, Leeches, and Eunice members of one class, has no more connection with their habitat, than the peculiarities of structure which unite Man, Monkeys, Bats, Lions, Seals, Beavers, Mice, and Whales into one class. Moreover, animals of different types living in the same element have no sort of similarity, as to size. The aquatic Insects, the aquatic Mollusks fall in with the average size of their class, as well as the aquatic Reptiles and the aquatic Birds, or the aquatic Mammalia; but there is no common average for either terrestrial or aquatic animals of different classes taken together, and in this lies the evidence that organized beings are independent of the mediums in which they live, as far as their origin is concerned, though it is plain that when created they were made to suit the element in which they were placed.

To me these facts show, that the phenomena of life are manifested in the physical world, and not through or by it; that organized beings are made to conquer and assimilate to themselves the materials of the inorganic world; that they maintain their original characteristics, notwithstanding the unceasing action of physical agents upon them. And I confess I cannot comprehend how beings, so entirely independent of these influences, could be produced by them.

SECTION XV: *Permanency of Specific Peculiarities in All Organized Beings.*

It was a great step in the progress of science when it was ascertained that species have fixed characters, and that they do not change in the course of time. But this fact, for which we are indebted to Cuvier, has acquired a still greater importance since it has also been established, that even the most extraordinary changes in the mode of existence and in the conditions under which animals may be placed, have no more influence upon their essential characters than the lapse of time.

The facts bearing upon these two subjects are too well known now to require special illustration. I will, therefore, allude only to a few points, to avoid even the possibility of a misapprehension of my statements. That animals of different geological periods differ specifically, *en masse*, from those of preceding or following formations, is a fact satisfactorily ascertained. Between two successive geological periods, then, changes have taken place among animals and plants. But none of those primordial forms of life, which naturalists call species, are known to have changed during any of these periods. It cannot be denied, that the species of different successive periods are supposed by some naturalists to derive their distinguishing features from changes which have taken place in those of preceding ages; but this is a mere supposition, supported neither by physiological nor by geological evidence, and the assumption that animals and plants may change in a similar manner during one and the same period, is equally gratuitous. On the contrary, it is known by the evidence furnished by the Egyptian monuments, and by the most careful comparison between animals found in the tombs of Egypt with living specimens of the same species obtained in the same country, that there is not the shadow of a difference between them, for a period of about five thousand years. These comparisons, first instituted by Cuvier, have proved, that as far as it has been possible to carry back the investigation, it does not afford the beginning of an evidence that species change in the course of time, if the comparisons be limited to the same great cosmic epoch. Geology only shows that at different periods[12] there have existed different species; but no transition from those of a preceding into those of the following epoch has ever been noticed anywhere; and the question alluded to here is to be distinguished from that of the origin of the differences in the bulk of species belonging to two different geological eras. The question we are now examining involves only the fixity or mutability of species during one epoch, one era, one period in the history of our globe. And nothing furnishes the slightest argument in favor of their mutability; on the contrary, every modern investigation has only gone to confirm the results first obtained by Cuvier, and his views that species are fixed.

It is something to be able to show my monumental evidence, and by direct comparison, that animals and plants have undergone no change for a period of about five thousand years. This result has had the greatest influence upon the progress of science, especially with reference to the consequences to be drawn from the occurrence in the series of geological formations of organized beings as highly diversified in each epoch as those of the present day; it has laid the foundation for the conviction, now universal among well informed naturalists, that this globe has been in existence for innumerable ages, and that the length of time elapsed since it first became inhabited cannot be counted in years. Even the length of the period to which we belong is still a problem, notwithstanding the precision with which certain systems of chronology would fix the creation of man. There are, however, many circumstances which show that the animals now living have been for a much longer period inhabitants of our globe than is generally supposed. It has been possible to trace the formation and growth of our coral reefs, especially in Florida, with sufficient precision to ascertain that it must take about eight thousand years for one of those coral walls to rise from its foundation to the level of the surface of the ocean. There are, around the southernmost extremity of Florida alone, four such reefs concentric with one another, which can be shown to have grown up, one after the other. This gives for the beginning of the first of these reefs an age of over thirty thousand years; and yet the corals by which they were all built up are the same identical species in all of them. These facts, then, furnish as direct evidence as we can obtain in any branch of physical inquiry, that some, at least, of the species of animals now existing, have been in existence over thirty thousand years, and have not undergone the slightest change during the whole of that period.[13] And yet these four concentric reefs are only the most distinct of that region; others, less extensively investigated thus far, lie to the northward; indeed, the whole peninsula of Florida consists altogether of coral reefs annexed to one another in the course of time, and containing only fragments of corals and shells, etc., identical with those now living upon that coast. Now, if a width of five miles is a fair average for one coral reef growing under the circumstances under which the concentric reefs of Florida are seen now to follow one another, and this regular succession should extend only as far north as Lake Ogeechobee, for two degrees of latitude, this would give about two hundred thousand years for the period of time which was necessary for that part of the peninsula of Florida which lies south of Lake Ogeechobee to rise to its present southern extent above the level of the sea, and during which no changes have taken place in the character of the animals of the Gulf of Mexico.

It is very prejudicial to the best interests of science to confound questions that are entirely different, merely for the sake of supporting a theory; yet this is constantly done, whenever the question of the fixity of species is alluded to. A few more words upon this point, will, therefore, not be out of place here.

I will not enter into a discussion upon the question whether any species is found identically the same in two successive formations, as I have already examined it at full length elsewhere, and it may be settled finally one way or the other, without affecting the proposition now under consideration; for it is plain, that if such identity could be proved, it would only show more satisfactorily how tenacious species are in their character, to continue to live through all the physical changes which have taken place between two successive geological periods. Again, such identity once proved, would leave it still doubtful whether their repre-

sentatives in two successive epochs are descendants one of the
other, as we have already strong evidence in favor of the separate
origin of the representative of the same species in separate geographical areas. The case of closely allied, but different species
occurring in successive periods, yet limited respectively in their
epochs, afford, in the course of time, a parallel to the case
of closely allied, so-called, representative species occupying different areas in space, which no sound naturalist would suppose
now to be derived one from the other. There is no more reason
to suppose equally allied species following one another in time to
be derived one from the other; and all that has been said in preceding paragraphs respecting the differences observed between
species occurring in different geographical areas, applies with the
same force to species succeeding each other in the course of time.

When domesticated animals and cultivated plants are mentioned as furnishing evidence of the mutability of species, the
circumstance is constantly overlooked or passed over in silence,
that the first point to be established respecting them, in order to
justify any inference from them against the fixity of species,
would be to show that each of them has originated from one common stock, which, far from being the case, is flatly contradicted
by the positive knowledge we have that the varieties of several
of them, at least, are owing to the entire amalgamation of different species. The Egyptian monuments show further that many of
those so-called varieties which are supposed to be the product of
time, are as old as any other animals which have been known to
man; at all events, we have no tradition, no monumental evidence
of the existence of any wild animal older than that which represents domesticated animals, already as different among themselves as they are now. It is, therefore, quite possible that the different races of domesticated animals were originally distinct
species, more or less mixed now, as the different races of men
are. Moreover, neither domesticated animals nor cultivated
plants, nor the races of men, are the proper subjects for an investigation respecting the fixity or mutability of species, as all
involve already the question at issue in the premises which are
assumed in introducing them as evidence in the case. With reference to the different breeds of our domesticated animals, which

are known to be produced by the management of man, as well as certain varieties of our cultivated plants, they must be well distinguished from permanent races, which, for aught we know, may be primordial; for breeds are the result of the fostering care of man; they are the product of the limited influence and control the human mind has over organized beings, and not the free product of mere physical agents. They show, therefore, that even the least important changes which may take place during one and the same cosmic period among animals and plants are controlled by an intellectual power, and do not result from the immediate action of physical causes.

So far, then, from disclosing the effects of physical agents, whatever changes are known to take place in the course of time among organized beings appear as the result of an intellectual power, and go, therefore, to substantiate the view that all the differences observed among finite beings are ordained by the action of the Supreme Intellect, and not determined by physical causes. This position is still more strengthened when we consider that the differences which exist between different races of domesticated animals and the varieties of our cultivated plants, as well as among the races of men, are permanent under the most diversified climatic influences; a fact, which the extensive migrations of the civilized nations daily proves more extensively, and which stands in direct contradiction to the supposition that such or similar influences could have produced them.

When considering the subject of domestication, in particular, it ought further to be remembered, that every race of men has its own peculiar kinds of domesticated animals and of cultivated plants, which exhibit much fewer varieties among them in proportion as those races of men have had little or no intercourse with other races, than the domesticated animals of those nations which have been formed by the mixture of several tribes.

It is often stated that the ancient philosophers have solved satisfactorily all the great questions interesting to man, and that modern investigations, though they have grasped with new vigor, and illuminated with new light, all the phenomena of the material world, have added little or nothing in the field of intellectual progress. Is this true? There is no question so deeply interesting to man as that of his own origin, and the origin of all things. And yet antiquity had no knowledge concerning it; things were formerly believed either to be from eternity, or to have been created at one time. Modern science, however, can show, in the most satisfactory manner, that all finite beings have made their appearance successively and at long intervals, and that each kind of organized beings has existed for a definite period of time in past ages, and that those now living are of comparatively recent origin. At the same time, the order of their succession and their immutability during such cosmic periods, show no causal connection with physical agents and the known sphere of action of these agents in nature, but argue in favor of repeated interventions on the part of the Creator. It seems really surprising, that while such an intervention is admitted by all, except the strict materialists, for the establishment of the laws regulating the inorganic world, it is yet denied by so many physicists, with reference to the introduction of organized beings at different successive periods. Does this not rather go to show the imperfect acquaintance of these investigators with the conditions under which life is manifested, and with the essential difference there is between the phenomena of the organic and those of the physical world, than to furnish any evidence that the organic world is the product of physical causes?

SECTION XVI: *Relations Between Animals and Plants and the Surrounding World.*

Every animal and plant stands in certain definite relations to the surrounding world, some however, like the domestic animals and cultivated plants, being capable of adapting themselves to various conditions more readily than others; but even this pliability is a characteristic feature. These relations are highly important in a systematic point of view, and deserve the most careful attention, on the part of naturalists. Yet, the direction zoological studies have taken since comparative anatomy and

embryology began to absorb almost entirely the attention of naturalists, has been very unfavorable to the investigation of the
habits of animals, in which their relations to one another and to
the conditions under which they live, are more especially exhibited. We have to go back to the authors of the preceding century, for the most interesting accounts of the habits of animals,
as among modern writers there are few who have devoted their
chief attention to this subject. So little, indeed, is its importance
now appreciated, that the students of this branch of natural history are hardly acknowledged as peers by their fellow investigators, the anatomists and physiologists, or the systematic zoologists. And yet, without a thorough knowledge of the habits of
animals, it will never be possible to ascertain with any degree of
precision the true limits of all those species which descriptive
zoologists have of late admitted with so much confidence in their
works. And after all, what does it matter to science that thousands of species more or less, should be described and entered in
our systems, if we know nothing about them? A very common
defect of the works relating to the habits of animals has no doubt
contributed to detract from their value and to turn the attention
in other directions: their purely anecdotic character, or the circumstance that they are too frequently made the occasion for
narrating personal adventures. Nevertheless, the importance of
this kind of investigation can hardly be overrated; and it would
be highly desirable that naturalists should turn again their attention that way, now that Comparative Anatomy and Physiology,
as well as Embryology, may suggest so many new topics of inquiry, and the progress of Physical Geography has laid such a
broad foundation for researches of this kind. Then we may learn
with more precision, how far the species described from isolated
specimens are founded in nature, or how far they may be only a
particular stage of growth of other species; then we shall know,
what is yet too little noticed, how extensive the range of variations is among animals, observed in their wild state, or rather how
much individuality there is in each and all living beings.
So marked, indeed, is this individuality in many families—and
that of Turtles affords a striking example of this kind—that correct descriptions of species can hardly be drawn from isolated

specimens, as is constantly attempted to be done. I have seen hundreds of specimens of some of our Chelonians, among which there were not two identical. And truly, the limits of this variability constitutes one of the most important characters of many species; and without precise information upon this point for every genus, it will never be possible to have a solid basis for the distinction of species. Some of the most perplexing questions in Zoology and Palaeontology might long ago have been settled, had we had more precise information upon this point, and were it better known how unequal in this respect different groups of the animal kingdom are, when compared with one another. While the individuals of some species seem all different, and might be described as different species, if seen isolated or obtained from different regions, those of other species appear all as cast in one and the same mould. It must be, therefore, at once obvious, how different the results of the comparison of one fauna with another may be, if the species of one have been studied accurately for a long period by resident naturalists, and the other is known only from specimens collected by chance travellers; or, if the fossil representatives of one period are compared with living animals, without both faunae having been first revised according to the same standard.

Another deficiency, in most works relating to the habits of animals, consists in the absence of general views and of comparisons. We do not learn from them, how far animals related by their structure are similar in their habits, and how far these habits are the expression of their structure. Every species is described as if it stood alone in the world; its peculiarities are mostly exaggerated, as if to contrast more forcibly with all others. Yet, how interesting would be a comparative study of the mode of life of closely allied species; how instructive a picture might be drawn of the resemblance there is in this respect between species of the same genus and of the same family. The more I learn upon this subject, the more am I struck with the similarity in the very movements, the general habits, and even in the intonation of the voices of animals belonging to the same family; that is to say, between animals agreeing in the main in form, size, structure, and mode of development. A minute study of these habits, of these movements, of the voice of animals cannot fail, therefore, to throw additional light upon their natural affinities.

While I thus acknowledge the great importance of such investigations with reference to the systematic arrangement of animals, I cannot help regretting deeply, that they are not more highly valued with reference to the information they might secure respecting the animals themselves, independently of any system. How much is there not left to study with respect to every species, after it is named and classified. No one can read Nauman's Natural History of the German Birds without feeling that natural history would be much further advanced, if the habits of all other animals had been as accurately investigated and as minutely recorded; and yet that work contains hardly any thing of importance with reference to the systematic arrangement of birds. We scarcely possess the most elementary information necessary to discuss upon a scientific basis the question of the instincts and in general the faculties of animals, and to compare them together and with those of man, not only because so few animals have been thoroughly investigated, but because so much fewer still have been watched during their earlier periods of life, when their faculties are first developing; and yet how attractive and instructive this growing age is in every living being! Who could, for instance, believe for a moment longer that the habits of animals are in any degree determined by the circumstances under which they live, after having seen a little Turtle of the genus Chelydra, still enclosed in its egg-shell, which it hardly fills half-way, with a yolk bag as large as itself hanging from its lower surface and enveloped in its amnios and in its allantois, with the eyes shut, snapping as fiercely as if it could bite without killing itself? Who can watch the Sunfish (*Pomotis vulgaris*) hovering over its eggs and protecting them for weeks, or the Catfish (*Pimelodus Catus*) move about with its young, like a hen with her brood, without remaining satisfied that the feeling which prompts them in these acts is of the same kind as that which attaches the Cow to her suckling, or the child to its mother? Who is the investigator, who having once recognized such a similarity between certain faculties of Man and those of the higher animals can feel prepared, in the present stage of our knowledge, to trace the limit where this community of nature ceases? And yet to ascertain the character of all these faculties there is but one road, the study of the habits of animals, and a comparison between them and the earlier stages of development of Man. I confess I could not say in what the mental faculties of a child differ from those of a young Chimpanzee.

Now that we have physical maps of almost every part of the globe, exhibiting the average temperature of the whole year and of every season upon land and sea; now that the average elevation of the continents above the sea, and that of the most characteristic parts of their surface, their valleys, their plains, their table-lands, their mountain systems, are satisfactorily known; now that the distribution of moisture in the atmosphere, the limits of the river systems, the prevailing direction of the winds, the course of the currents of the ocean, are not only investigated, but mapped down, even in school atlases; now that the geological structure of nearly all parts of the globe has been determined with tolerable precision, zoologists have the widest field and the most accurate basis to ascertain all the relations which exist between animals and the world in which they live.

Having thus considered the physical agents with reference to the share they may have had in calling organized beings into existence, and satisfied ourselves that they are not the cause of their origin, it now remains for us to examine more particularly these relations, as an established fact, as conditions in which animals and plants are placed at the time of their creation, within definite limits of action and reaction between them; for though not produced by the influence of the physical world, organized beings live in it, they are born in it, they grow up in it, they multiply in it, they assimilate it to themselves or feed upon it, they have even a modifying influence upon it to themselves or feed upon it, they have even a modifying influence upon it within the same limits, as the physical world is subservient to every manifestation of their life. It cannot fail, therefore, to be highly interesting and instructive to trace these connections, even without any reference to the manner in which they were established, and this is the proper sphere of investigation in the study of the habits of animals. The behavior of each kind towards its fellow-beings, and with reference to the conditions of existence in which it is placed, constitutes a field of inquiry of the deepest interest, as extensive as it is complicated. When properly investigated, especially within the sphere which constitutes more particularly the essential characteristics of each species of animals and plants, it is likely to afford the most direct evidence of the unexpected independence of physical influences of organized beings, if I mistake not the evidence I have myself been able to collect. What can there be more characteristic of different species of animals than their motions, their plays, their affections, their sexual relations, their care of their young, the dependence of these upon their parents, their instincts, etc., etc.; and yet there is nothing in all this which depends in the slightest degree upon the nature or the influence of the physical conditions in which they live. Even their organic functions are independent of these conditions to a degree unsuspected, though this is the sphere of their existence which exhibits the closest connections with the world around.

Functions have so long been considered as the test of the character of organs, that it has almost become an axiom in Comparative Anatomy and Physiology, that identical functions presuppose identical organs. Most of our general works upon Comparative Anatomy are divided into chapters according to this view. And yet there never was a more incorrect principle, leading to more injurious consequences, more generally adopted. That naturalists should not long ago have repudiated it, is the more surprising as every one must have felt again and again how unsound it is. The organs of respiration and circulation of fishes afford a striking example. How long have not their gills been considered as the equivalent of the lungs of the higher Vertebrata, merely because they are breathing organs; and yet these gills are formed in a very different way from the lungs; they bear very different relations to the vascular system; and it is now known that they may exist simultaneously with lungs, as in some full-grown Batrachians, and, in the earlier embryonic stages of development, in all Vertebrata. There can no longer be any doubt now, that they are essentially different organs, and that their functions afford no test of their nature and cannot constitute an argu-

ment in favor of their organic identity. The same may be said of
the vascular system of the fishes. Cuvier described their heart as
representing the right auricle and the right ventricle, because it
propels the blood it contains to the gills, in the same manner as
the right ventricle propels the blood to the lungs of the warm
blooded animals; yet Embryology has taught us that such a comparison based upon the special relations of the heart of fishes, is
unjustifiable. The air sacs of certain spiders have also been considered as lungs, because they perform similar respiratory functions, and yet they are only modified tracheae, which are constructed upon such a peculiar plan, and stand in such different
relations to the peculiar kind of blood of the Articulata, that no
homology can be traced between them and the lungs of Vertebrata, no more than between the so-called lungs of the air breathing Mollusks, whose aerial respiratory cavity is only a modification
of the peculiar kind of gills observed in other Mollusks. Examples
might easily be multiplied; I will, however, only allude further
to the alimentary canal of Insects and Crustacea, with its glandu-
lar appendages, formed in such a different way from that of
Vertebrata, or Mollusks, or Radiata, to their legs and wings, etc.,
etc. I might allude also to what has been called the foot in Mollusks, did it not appear like pretending to suppose that any one
entertains still an idea that such a name implies any similarity
between their locomotive apparatus and that of Vertebrata or
Articulata, and yet, the very use of such a name misleads the
student, and even some of the coryphees of our science have not
freed themselves of such and similar extravagant comparisons,
especially with reference to the solid parts of the frame of the
lower animals.

The identification of functions and organs was a natural consequence of the prevailing ideas respecting the influence physical
agents were supposed to have upon organized beings. But as
soon as it is understood, how different the organs may be, which
in animals perform the same function, organization is at once
brought into such a position to physical agents as makes it utterly
impossible to maintain any genetic connection between them. A
fish, a crab, a mussel, living in the same waters, breathing at the
same source, should have the same respiratory organs, if the

elements in which these animals live had any thing to do with shaping their organization. I suppose no one can be so short-sighted, as to assume that the same physical agents acting upon animals of different types, must produce, in each, peculiar organs, and not to perceive that such an assumption implies the very existence of these animals, independently of the physical agents. But this mistake recurs so constantly in discussions upon this and similar topics, that, trivial as it is, it requires to be rebuked. On the contrary, when acknowledging an intellectual conception, as the preliminary step in the existence not only of all organized beings, but of every thing in nature, how natural to find that while diversity is introduced in the plan, in the complication and the details of structure of animals, their relations to the surrounding media are equally diversified, and consequently the same functions may be performed by the most different apparatus!

SECTION XVII: *Relations of Individuals to One Another.*

The relations in which individuals of the same species of animals stand to one another are not less determined and fixed than the relations of species to the surrounding elements, which we have thus far considered. The relations which individual animals bear to one another are of such a character, that they ought long ago to have been considered as proof sufficient that no organized being could ever have been called into existence by another agency than the direct intervention of a reflective mind. It is in a measure conceivable that physical agents might produce something like the body of the lowest kinds of animals or plants, and that under identical circumstances the same thing may have been produced again and again, by the repetition of the same process; but that upon closer analysis of the possibilities of the case, it should not have at once appeared how incongruous the further supposition is, that such agencies could delegate the power of reproducing what they had just called into existence, to those very beings, with such limitations, that they could never reproduce any thing but themselves, I am at a loss to understand. It will no more do to suppose that from simpler structures such a process may end in the production of the most perfect, as every step implies an addition of possibilities not even included in the original case. Such a delegation of power can only be an act of intelligence; while between the production of an indefinite number of organized beings, as the result of a physical law, and the reproduction of these same organized beings by themselves, there is no necessary connection. The successive generations of any animal or plant cannot stand, as far as their origin is concerned, in any causal relation to physical agents, if these agents have not the power of delegating their own action to the full extent to which they have already been productive in the first appearance of these beings; for it is a physical law that the resultant is equal to the forces applied. If any new being has ever been produced by such agencies, how could the successive generations enter, at the time of their birth, into the same relations to these agents, as their ancestors, if these beings had not in themselves the faculty of sustaining their character, in spite of these agents? Why, again, should animals and plants at once begin to decompose under the very influence of all those agents which have been subservient to the maintenance of their life, as soon as life ceases, if life is limited or determined by them?

There exist between individuals of the same species relations far more complicated than those already alluded to, which go still further to disprove any possibility of causal dependence of organized beings upon physical agents. The relations upon which the maintenance of species is based, throughout the animal kingdom, in the universal antagonism of sex, and the infinite diversity of these connections in different types, have really nothing to do with external conditions of existence; they indicate only relations of individuals, beyond their connections with the material world in which they live. How, then, could these relations be the result of physical causes, when physical agents are known to have a specific sphere of action, in no way bearing upon this sphere of phenomena?

For the most part, the relations of individuals to individuals are unquestionably of an organic nature, and, as such have to be viewed in the same light as any other structural feature; but there is much, also, in these connections that partakes of a psychological character, taking this expression in the widest sense of the word.

When animals fight with one another, when they associate for a common purpose, when they warn one another in danger, when they come to the rescue of one another, when they display pain or joy, they manifest impulses of the same kind as are considered among the moral attributes of man. The range of their passions is even as extensive as that of the human mind, and I am at a loss to perceive a difference of kind between them, however much they may differ in degree and in the manner in which they are expressed. The gradations of the moral faculties among the higher animals and man are, moreover, so imperceptible, that to deny to the first a certain sense of responsibility and consciousness, would certainly be an exaggeration of the difference between animals and man. There exists, besides, as much individuality, within their respective capabilities, among animals as among men, as every sportsman, or every keeper of menageries, or every farmer and shepherd can testify who has had a large experience with wild, or tamed, or domesticated animals.

This argues strongly in favor of the existence in every animal of an immaterial principle similar to that which, by its excellence and superior endowments, places man so much above animals.[14] Yet the principle exists unquestionably, and whether it be called soul, reason, or instinct, it presents in the whole range of organized beings a series of phenomena closely linked together; and upon it are based not only the higher manifestations of the mind, but the very permanence of the specific differences which characterize every organism. Most of the arguments of philosophy in favor of the immortality of man apply equally to the permanency of this principle in other living beings. May I not add, that a future life, in which man should be deprived of that great source of enjoyment and intellectual and moral improvement which result from the contemplation of the harmonies of an organic world, would involve a lamentable loss, and may we not look to a spiritual concert of the combined worlds and all their inhabitants in presence of their Creator as the highest conception of paradise.

SECTION XVIII: *Metamorphoses of Animals.*

The study of Embryology is of very recent date; the naturalists of the past century, instead of investigating the phenomena accompanying the first formation and growth of animals, were satisfied with vague theories upon reproduction. It is true the metamorphoses of Insects became very early the subject of most remarkable observations, but so little was it then known that all animals undergo great changes from the first to the last stages of their growth, that metamorphosis was considered a distinguishing character of Insects. The differences between Insects, in that respect, are however already so great, that a distinction was introduced between those which undergo a complete metamorphosis, that is to say, which appear in three successive different forms, as larvae, pupae, and perfect insects, and those with an incomplete metamorphosis, or whose larvae differ little from the perfect insect. The range of these changes is yet so limited in some insects, that it is not only not greater, but is even much smaller than in many representatives of other classes. We may, therefore, well apply the term metamorphosis to designate all the changes which animals undergo, in direct and immediate succession,[15] during their growth, whether these changes are great or small, provided they are correctly qualified for each type.

The study of Embryology, at first limited to the investigation of the changes which the chicken undergoes in the egg, has gradually extended to every type of the animal kingdom; and so diligent and thorough has been the study, that the first author who ventured upon an extensive illustration of the whole field, C. E. von Baer, has already presented the subject in such a clear manner, and drawn general conclusions so accurate and so comprehensive, that all subsequent researches in this department of our science, may be considered only as a further development of the facts first noticed by him and of the results he has already deduced from them. It was he who laid the foundation for the most extensive generalizations respecting the mode of formation of animals; for he first discovered, in 1827, the ovarian egg of Mammalia, and thus showed for the first time, that there is no essential difference in the mode of reproduction of the so-called viviparous and oviparous animals, and that man himself is developed in the same manner as the animals. The universal presence of eggs in all animals and in the unity of their structure, which was soon afterwards fully ascertained, constitute, in my opinion, the greatest discovery of modern times in the natural sciences.

It was, indeed, a gigantic step to demonstrate such an identity in the material basis of the development of all animals, when their anatomical structure was already known to exhibit such radically different plans in their full-grown state. From that time a more and more extensive investigation of the manner in which the first germ is formed in these eggs, and the embryo develops itself; how its organs grow gradually out of a homogeneous mass; what changes, what complications, what connections, what functions they exhibit at every stage; how in the end the young animal assumes its final form and structure, and becomes a new, independent being, could not fail to be the most interesting subject of inquiry. To ascertain all this, in as many animals as possible, belonging to the most different types of the animal kingdom, became soon the principal aim of all embryological investigations; and it can truly be said, that few sciences have advanced with such astonishing rapidity, and led to more satisfactory results.

For the actual phases of the mode of development of the different types of the animal kingdom, I must refer to the special works upon this subject, no general treatise embracing the most recent investigations having as yet been published; and I must take it for granted, that before forming a definite opinion upon the comparisons instituted hereafter between the growth of animals, and the structural gradation among full-grown animals, or the order of succession of the fossils characteristic of different geological periods, the necessary information respecting these changes has been gathered by my readers, and sufficiently mastered to enable them to deal with it freely.

The embryology of Polypi has been very little studied thus far; what we know of the embryonic growth of these animals relates chiefly to the family of Actinoids. When the young is hatched, it has the form of a little club-shaped or pear-shaped body, which soon assumes the appearance of the adult, from which it differs only by having few tentacles. The mode of ramification and the multiplication by buds have, however, been carefully and minutely studied in all the families of this class. Acalephs present phenomena so peculiar, that they are discussed hereafter in a special section. Their young are either polyplike or resemble more immediately the type of their class. Few multiply in a direct, progressive development. As to Echinoderms, they have for a long time almost entirely escaped the attention of Embryologists, but lately J. Muller has published a series of most important investigations upon this class, disclosing a wonderful diversity is the modes of their development, not only in the different orders of the class, but even in different genera of the same family. The larvae of many have a close resemblance to diminutive Ctenophorae, and may be homologized with this type of Acalephs.

As I shall hereafter refer frequently to the leading divisions of the animal kingdom, I ought to state here, that I do not adopt some of the changes which have been proposed lately in the limitation of the classes, and which seem to have been pretty generally received with favor. The undivided type of Radiata appears to me as one of the most natural branches of the animal kingdom, and I consider its subdivision into Coelenterata and Echinodermata, as an exaggeration of the anatomical differences observed between them. As far as the plan of their structure is concerned, they do not differ at all, and that structure is throughout homological. In this branch I recognize only three classes, *Polypi, Acalephae,* and *Echinodermata*. The chief difference between the two first lies in the radiating partitions of the main cavity of the Polypi, supporting the reproductive organs; moreover, the digestive cavity in this class consists of an inward fold of the upper aperture of the common sac of the body, while in Acalephs there

exist radiating tubes, at least in the *proles medusina,* which extend to the margin of the body where they anastomoze, and the
digestive cavity is hollowed out of the gelatinous mass of
the body. This is equally true of the Hydroids, the Medusae
proper, and the Ctenophorae; but nothing of the kind is observed
among Polypi. Siphonophorae, whether their *proles medusina*
becomes free or not, and Hydroids agree in having, in the *proles
medusina,* simple radiating tubes, uniting into a single circular
tube around the margin of the bell-shaped disk. These two
groups, constitute together, one natural order, in contradistinction from the Covered-eyed Medusae, whose radiating tubes
ramify towards the margin and form a complicated net of anas-
tomoses. Morphologically, the *proles polypoidea* of the Acalephs,
is as completely an Acaleph, as their *proles medusina,* and
whether they separate or remain connected, their structural relations are everywhere the same. A comparison of Hydractinia,
which is the most common and the most polymorphous Hydroid,
with our common Portuguese Man-of-War (*Physalia,*) may at
once show the homology of their most polymorphous individuals.

The embryology of Mollusks has been very extensively investigated, and some types of this branch are among the very best
known in the animal kingdom. The natural limits of the branch
itself appear, however, somewhat doubtful. I hold that it must
include the Bryozoa, which lead gradually through the Brachiopods and Tunicata to the ordinary Acephala, and I would add,
that I have satisfied myself of the propriety of uniting the Vorti-
cellidae with Bryozoa. On the other hand, the Cephalopods can
never be separated from the Mollusks proper, as a distinct
branch; the partial segmentation of their yolk no more affords a
ground for their separation, than the total segmentation of the
yolk of Mammalia would justify their separation from the other
Vertebrata. Moreover, Cephalopods are in all the details of their
structure homologous with the other Mollusks. The Tunicata are
particularly interesting, inasmuch as the simple Ascidians have
pedunculated young, which exhibit the most striking resemblance
to Boltenia, and form, at the same time, a connecting link with
the compound Ascidians. The development of the Lamellibranchiata seems to be very uniform, but they differ greatly as to their

breeding, many laying their eggs before the germ is formed, whilst others carry them in their gills until the young are entirely formed. This is observed particularly among the Unios, some of which, however, lay their eggs very early, while others carry them for a longer or shorter time, in a special pouch of the outer gill, which presents the most diversified forms in different genera of this family. Nothing is as yet known of the development of Brachiopods. The Gasteropods exhibit a much greater diversity in their development than the Lamellibranchiata. Even among the terrestrial and aquatic Pulmonata there are striking differences. Some of the Pectinibranchiata are remarkable for curious cases in which their eggs are hatched and the young developed, to an advanced state of growth. The cases of Pyrula and Strombus are among the most extraordinary of these organic nests. The embryology of Cephalopods has been masterly illustrated by Kölliker.

There is still much diversity of opinion among naturalists, respecting the limits of Articulata; some being inclined to separate the Arthropoda and Worms as distinct branches, while others unite them into one. I confess I cannot see the ground for a distinction. The worm-like nature of the larvae of the majority of Arthropods and the perfect homology of these larvae with the true Worms, seem to me to show beyond the possibility of a doubt, that all these animals are built upon one and the same plan, and belong, therefore, to one branch, which contains only three classes, if the principles laid down in my second chapter are at all correct, namely, the Worms, Crustacea, and Insects. As to the Protozoa, I have little confidence in the views generally entertained respecting their nature. Having satisfied myself that Colpoda and Paramecium are the brood of Planariae, and Opalina that of Distoma, I see no reason, why the other Infusoria, included in Ehrenberg's division Enterodela, should not also be the brood of the many lower Worms, the development of which has thus far escaped our attention. Again, a comparison of the early stages of development of the Entomostraca with Rotifera might be sufficient to show, what Burmeister, Dana, and Leydig have proved in another way, that Rotifera are genuine Crustacea, and not Worms. The vegetable character of most of the Anentera has been satisfactorily illustrated. I have not yet been able to arrive at a definite result respecting the Rhizopods, though they may represent, in the type of Mollusks, the stage of yolk segmentation of Gasteropods. From these remarks it should be inferred, that I do not consider the Protozoa as a distinct branch of the animal kingdom, nor the Infusoria as a natural class.

Taking the class of Worms, in the widest sense, it would thus embrace the Helminths, Turbellariae, and Annulata. The embryology of these animals still requires careful study, notwithstanding the many extensive investigations to which they have been submitted; the intestinal Worms especially continue to baffle the zeal of naturalists, even now when the leading features of their development are ascertained. The Nematoids undergo a very simple development, without alternate generations, and as some are viviparous their changes can easily be traced. The Cestods and Cystici, which were long considered as separate orders of Helminths, are now known to stand in direct genetic connection with one another, the Cystici being only earlier stages of development of the Cestods. The Trematods exhibit the most complicated phenomena of alternate generations; but as no single species has thus far been traced through all the successive stages of its transformations, doubts are still entertained respecting the genetic connection of many of the forms which appear to belong to the same organic cycle. It is also still questionable, whether Gregarinae and Psorospermia are embryonic forms or not, though the most recent investigations render it probable that they are. The development of the Annulata, as they are now circumscribed, exhibits great variety; some resemble more the Nematods, in their metamorphoses, while others, the Leeches, for instance, approximate more the type of the Trematods. The Sipunculoids appear to be more closely related to the Annulata than to the Holothurioids.

The class of Crustacea, on the contrary, may be considered as one of the best known, as far as its zoological characters and embryonic growth are concerned; the only point still questioned being the relationship of the Rotifera. In their mode of development the Lernaeans, the Entomostraca proper, and the Cirripeds agree as closely with one another as they differ from the higher Crustacea. This conformity is the more interesting, as the low position the Entomostraca hold in the class of Crustacea, agrees strikingly with their early appearance in geological times, while the form of the adult Cirripeds and that of the Lernaeans would hardly lead one to suspect their near relationship, which has, indeed, been quite overlooked until Embryology showed that their true position is among Crustacea. In the development of the higher Crustacea, their superior rank is plainly exhibited, and few types show more directly a resemblance, in their early stages of development, to the lower members of their class, than the Brachyura.

In the class of Insects, I include Myriapods, Arachnoids, and the true Insects, as, according to the views expressed hereafter, these natural groups constitute only different degrees of complication of the same combination of organic systems, and must, therefore, be considered as natural orders of one and the same class. This class, though very extensively studied in a zoological and anatomical point of view, and as far as the habits of its representatives are concerned, still requires, however, much patient work, as the early embryonic development of these animals has been much less studied than their later transformations. The type of the Arachnoids embraces two groups, the Acari and the Arachnoids proper, corresponding respectively in this class to the Entomostraca and the higher Crustacea. The embryo of the Acari resembles somewhat that of the Entomostraca, whilst that of the true Spiders recalls the metamorphosis of the higher Crustacea. On the ground of the similarity of their young, some animals, formerly referred to the class of Worms, are now considered as Arachnoids; but the limits between the aquatic Mites and the Pycnogonums are not yet quite defined.

In the branch of Vertebrata, all classes have been extensively studied, and as far as the principal types are concerned, the leading features of their development are satisfactorily known. Much, however, remains to be done to ascertain the minor modifications characteristic of the different families. It may even be, that further investigations will greatly modify the general classification of the whole branch. The class of Fishes may require subdivision, since the development of the Plagiostoms differs greatly from that of the ordinary fishes. As it now stands in our systems, the class of Fishes is certainly the most heterogeneous among Vertebrata. The disagreement of authors as to the limits and respective value of its orders and families may be partly owing to the unnatural circumscription of the class itself. As to the Reptiles, it is already certain, that the Amphibia and Reptiles proper, so long united as one class, constitute two distinct classes. In the main, the development of the true Reptiles agrees very closely with that of the Birds, while the Amphibians resemble more the true fishes. In no class are renewed embryological investigations, extending over a variety of families, so much needed, as in that of Birds, though the general development of these animals is, perhaps, better known than that of any other type; while the class of Mammalia has found in Bischoff a most successful and thorough investigator.

Embryology has, however, a wider scope than to trace the growth of individual animals, the gradual building up of their body, the formation of their organs, and all the changes they undergo in their structure and in their form; it ought also to embrace a comparison of these forms and the successive steps of these changes between all the types of the animal kingdom, in order to furnish definite standards of their relative standing, of their affinities, of the correspondence of their organs in all their parts. Embryologists have thus far considered too exclusively, the gradual transformation of the egg into a perfect animal; there remains still a wide field of investigation to ascertain the different degrees of similarity between the successive forms an animal assumes until it has completed its growth, and the various forms of different kinds of full-grown animals of the same type; between the different stages of complication of their structure in general, and the perfect structure of their kindred; between the successive steps in the formation of all their parts and the various degrees of perfection of the parts of other groups; between the normal course of the whole development of one type compared with that of other types, as well as between the ultimate histological differences which all exhibit within certain limits. Though important fragments have been contributed upon these different points, I know how much remains to be done, from the little I have as yet been able to gather myself, by systematic research in this direction.

I have satisfied myself long ago, that Embryology furnishes the most trustworthy standard to determine the relative rank among animals. A careful comparison of the successive stages of development of the higher Batrachians furnishes, perhaps, the most striking example of the importance of such investigations. The earlier stages of the Tadpole exemplify the structure and form of those Ichthyoids which have either no legs, or very imperfect legs, with and without external gills; next it assumes a shape reminding us more of the Tritons and Salamanders, and ends with the structure of the Frog or Toad. A comparison between the two latter families might prove further, that the Toads are higher than the Frogs, not only on account of their more terrestrial habits (see Sect. XVI), but because the embryonic web, which, to some extent, still unites the fingers in the Frogs, disappears entirely in the Toads, and may be also, because glands are developed in their skin, which do not exist in Frogs. A similar comparison of the successive changes of a new species of Comatula discovered by Prof. Holmes, in the harbor of Charleston, in South Carolina, has shown me in what relation the different types of Crinoids of past ages stand to these changes, and has furnished a standard to determine their relative rank; as it cannot be doubted, that the earlier stages of growth of an animal exhibit a condition of relative inferiority, when contrasted with what it grows to be, after it has completed its development, and before it enters upon those phases of its existence which constitute old age, and certain curious retrograde metamorphoses observed among parasites.

In the young Comatula there exists a stem, by which the little animal is attached, either to sea weeds, or to the cirrhi of the parent; the stem is at first simple and without cirrhi, supporting a globular head, upon which the so-called arms are next developed and gradually completed by the appearance of branches; a few cirrhi are, at the same time, developed upon the stem, which increase in number until they form a wreath between the arms and the stem. At last, the crown having assumed all the characters of a diminutive Comatula, drops off, freeing itself from the stem, and the Comatula moves freely as an independent animal.

The classes of Crustacea and of Insects, are particularly instructive in this respect. Rathke, however, had described the transformations of so many Crustacea, that I cannot do better than to refer to his various papers upon this subject, for details relating to the changes these animals undergo during their earlier stages of growth. I would only add, that while the embryo of the highest Crustacea, the Brachyura, resembles by its form and structure the lowest types of this class, as the Entomostraca and Isopoda, it next assumes the shape of those of a higher order, the Macroura, before it appears with all the characteristics of the Brachyura.

Embryology furnishes, also, the best measure of the true affinities existing between animals. I do not mean to say, that the affinities of animals can only be ascertained by embryonic investigations; the history of Zoology shows, on the contrary, that even before the study of the formation and growth of animals had become a distinct branch of physiology, the general relationship of most animals had already been determined, with a remarkable degree of accuracy, by anatomical investigations. It is, nevertheless, true, that in some remarkable instances, the knowledge of the embryonic changes of certain animals gave the first clue to their true affinities, while, in other cases, it has furnished a very welcome confirmation of relationships, which, before, could appear probable, but were still very problematical. Even Cuvier considered, for instance, the Barnacles as a distinct class, which he placed among Mollusks, under the name of Cirripeds. It was not until Thompson had shown, what was soon confirmed by Burmeister and Martin St. Ange, that the young Barnacle has a structure and form identical with that of some of the most common Entomostraca, that their true position in the system of animals could be determined; when they had to be removed to the class of Crustacea, among Articulata. The same was the case with the Lernaeans, which Cuvier arranged with the Intestinal Worms, and which Nordmann has shown upon embryological evidence to belong also to the class of Crustacea. Lamarck associated the

Crinoids with Polypi, and though they were removed to the class of Echinoderms by Cuvier, before the metamorphoses of the Comatula were known, the discovery of their pedunculated young furnished a direct proof that this was their true position.

Embryology affords further a test for homologies in contradistinction of analogies. It shows that true homologies are limited respectively within the natural boundaries of the great branches of the animal kingdom.

The distinction between homologies and analogies, upon which the English naturalists have first insisted, has removed much doubt respecting the real affinities of animals which could hardly have been so distinctly appreciated before. It has taught us to distinguish between real affinity, based upon structural conformity, and similarity, based upon mere external resemblance in form and habits. But even after this distinction had been fairly established, it remained to determine within what limits homologies may be traced. The works of Oken, Spix, Geoffroy, and Carus, show to what extravagant comparisons a preconceived idea of unity may lead. It was not until Baer had shown that the development of the four great branches of the animal kingdom is essentially different, that it could even be suspected that organs performing identical functions may be different in their essential relations to one another, and not until Rathke had demonstrated that the yolk is in open communication with the main cavity of the Articulata, on the dorsal side of the animal, and not on the ventral side, as in Vertebrata, that a solid basis was obtained for the natural limitation of true homologies. It now appears more and more distinctly, with every step of the progress Embryology is making, that the structure of animals is only homologous within the limits of the four great branches of the animal kingdom, and that general homology strictly proved, proves also typical identity, as special homology proves class identity.

The results of all embryonic investigations of modern times go to show more and more extensively, that animals are entirely independent of external causes in their development. The identity of the metamorphoses of oviparous and viviparous animals belonging to the same type, furnishes the most convincing evidence to that effect. Formerly it was supposed that the embryo could be affected directly by external influences to such an extent, that monstrosities, for instance, were ascribed to the influence of external causes. Direct observation has shown, that they are founded upon peculiarities of the normal course of their development. The snug berth in which the young undergo their first transformation in the womb of their mother in all Mammalia, excludes so completely the immediate influence of any external agent, that it is only necessary to allude to it, to show how independent their growth must be of the circumstances in which even the mother may be placed. This is equally true of all other viviparous animals, as certain snakes, certain sharks, and the viviparous fishes. Again, the uniformity of temperature in the nests of birds, and the exclusion, to a certain degree, of influences which might otherwise reach them, in the various structures animals build for the protection of their young or of their eggs, show distinctly, that the instinct of all animals leads them to remove their progeny from the influence of physical agencies, or to make these agents subservient to their purposes, as in the case of the ostrich. Reptiles and terrestrial Mollusks bury their eggs to subtract them from varying influences; fishes deposit them in localities where they are exposed to the least changes. Insects secure theirs in various ways. Most marine animals living in extreme climates, lay their eggs in winter, when the variations of external influences are reduced to a minimum. Everywhere we find evidence that the phenomena of life, though manifested in the midst of all the most diversified physical influences, are rendered independent of them to the utmost degree, by a variety of contrivances prepared by the animals themselves, in self-protection, or for the protection of their progeny from any influence of physical agents not desired by them, or not subservient to their own ends.

Notes

1. The expressions constantly used with reference to genera and species and the higher groups in our systems—as, Mr. A. *has made* such a species *a genus;* Mr. B. *employs* this or that species to *form his*

genus; and in which most naturalists indulge when speaking of *their* species, *their* genera, *their* families, *their* systems—exhibit in an unquestionable light the conviction, that such groups are of their own making; which can, however, only be true in so far as these groups are not true to nature, if the views I shall present below are at all correct.

2. A series of classifications of animals and plants, exhibiting each a natural system of the types known to have existed simultaneously during the several successive geological periods, considered singly and without reference to the types of other ages, would show in a strong light the different relations in which the classes, the orders, the families, and even the genera and species, have stood to one another during each epoch. Such classifications would illustrate, in the most impressive manner, the importance of an accurate knowledge of the relative standing of all animals and plants, which can only be inferred from the perusal even of those palaeontological works in which fossil remains are illustrated according to their association in different geological formations; for, in all these works, the remains of past ages are uniformly referred to a system established upon the study of the animals now living, thus lessening the impression of their peculiar combination for the periods under consideration.

3. It must not be overlooked here that a system may be natural, that is, may agree in every respect with the facts in nature, and yet not be considered by its author as the manifestation of the thoughts of a Creator, but merely as the expression of a fact existing in nature, no matter how, which the human mind may trace and reproduce in a systematic form of its own invention.

4. I allude here only to the doctrines of materialists; but I feel it necessary to add, that there are physicists, who might be shocked at the idea of being considered as materialists, who are yet prone to believe that when they have recognized the laws which regulate the physical world, and acknowledged that these laws were established by the Deity, they have explained every thing, even when they have considered only the phenomena of the inorganic world, as if the world contained no living beings and as if these living beings exhibited nothing that differed from the inorganic world. Mistaking for a causal relation the intellectual connection observable between serial phenomena, they are unable to perceive any difference between disorder and the free, independent, and self-possessed action of a superior mind, and call mysticism, even a passing allusion to the existence of an immaterial principle in animals, which they acknowledge themselves in man. [POWELL's Essays, etc., p. 478, 385, and 466.] I would further

remark, that, when speaking of creation in contradistinction with reproduction, I mean only to allude to the difference there is between the
regular course of phenomena in nature and the establishment of that
order of things, without attempting to explain either; for in whatever
manner any state of things which has prevailed for a time upon earth
may have been introduced, it is self-evident that its establishment and
its maintenance for a determined period are two very different things,
however frequently they may be mistaken as identical. It is further of
itself plain that the laws which may explain the phenomena of the
material world, in contradistinction from the organic, cannot be considered as accounting for the existence of living beings, even though
these have a material body, unless it be actually shown that the action
of these laws implies by their very nature the production of such
beings. Thus far, Cross's experiments are the only ones offered as
proving such a result. I do not know what physicists may think about
them now; but I know that there is scarcely a zoologist who doubts
that they only exhibited a mistake. Life in appropriating the physical
world to itself with all its peculiar phenomena exhibits, however, some
of its own and of a higher order, which cannot be explained by physical
agencies. The circumstance that life is so deeply rooted in the inorganic
nature, affords, nevertheless, a strong temptation to explain one by
the other; but we shall see presently how fallacious these attempts
have been.

    5. I am well aware that even the most eminent investigators
consider the task of science at an end, as soon as the most general
relations of natural phenomena have been ascertained. To many the
inquiry into the primitive cause of their existence seems either beyond
the reach of man, or as belonging rather to philosophy than to physics.
To these the name of God appears out of place in a scientific work,
as if the knowledge of secondary agencies constituted alone a worthy
subject for their investigations, and as if nature could teach nothing
about its Author. Many, again, are no doubt prevented from expressing
their conviction that the world was called into existence and is regulated by an intelligent God, either by the fear of being supposed to
share clerical or sectarian prejudices; or because it may be dangerous
for them to discuss freely such questions without acknowledging at the
same time the obligation of taking the Old Testament as the standard
by which the validity of their results is to be measured. Science,
however, can only prosper when confining itself within its legitimate
sphere; and nothing can be more detrimental to its true dignity than
discussions like those which took place at the last meeting of the
German association of naturalists, in Göttingen, and which have since

then been carried on in several pamphlets in which bigotry vies with personality and invective.

6. In order fully to appreciate the difficulty alluded to here, it is only necessary to remember how complicated, and at the same time how localized the conditions are under which animals multiply. The egg originates in a special organ, the ovary; it grows there to a certain size, until it requires fecundation, that is, the influence of another living being, or at least of the product of another organ, the spermary, to determine the further development of the germ, which, under the most diversified conditions, in different species, passes successively through all those changes which lead to the formation of a new perfect being. I then would ask, is it probable that the circumstances under which animals and plants originated for the first time can be much simpler, or even as simple, as the conditions necessary for their reproduction only, after they have once been created? Preliminary, then, to their first appearance, the conditions necessary for their growth must have been provided for, if, as I believe, they were created as eggs, which conditions must have been conformable to those in which the living representatives of the types first produced, now reproduce themselves. If it were assumed that they originated in a more advanced stage of life, the difficulties would be still greater, as a moment's consideration cannot fail to show, especially if it is remembered how complicated the structure of some of the animals was, which are known to have been among the first inhabitants of our globe. When investigating this subject, it is of course necessary to consider the first appearance of animals and plants, upon the basis of probabilities only, or even simply upon that of possibilities; as with reference to these first-born, at least, the transmutation theory furnishes no explanation of their existence.

For every species belonging to the first fauna and the first flora which have existed upon earth, special relations, special contrivances must therefore have been provided. Now, what would be appropriate for the one, would not suit the other, so that excluding one another in this way, they cannot have originated upon the same point; while within a wider area, physical agents are too uniform in their mode of action to have laid the foundation for so many such specific differences as existed between the first inhabitants of our globe.

7. Few geologists only may now be inclined to believe that the lowest strata known to contain fossils, are not the lowest deposits formed since the existence of organized beings upon earth. But even those who would assume that still lower fossiliferous beds may yet be discovered, or may have entirely disappeared by the influence of

plutonic agencies, (POWELL's Essays, etc., p. 424,) must acknowledge the fact that everywhere in the lowest rocks known to contain fossils at all, there is a variety of them found together. (See Sect. VII.) Moreover, the similarity in the character of the oldest fossils found in different parts of the world, goes far, in my opinion, to prove that we actually do know the earliest types of the animal kingdom which have inhabited our globe. This conclusion seems fully sustained by the fact that we find everywhere below this oldest set of fossiliferous beds, other stratified rocks in which no trace of organized beings can be found.

8. Acalephs have been found in the Jurassic Limestone of Solenhofen; their absence in other formations may be owing simply to the extraordinary softness of their body. Insects are known as early as the Carboniferous Formation, and may have existed before.

9. The human race affords an example of the wide distribution of a terrestrial type; the Herring and the Mackerel families have an equally wide distribution in the sea. The Mammalia of New Holland show how some families may be limited to one continent; the family of *Labyrinthici* of the Indian Ocean, how fishes may be circumscribed in the sea, and that of the Goniodonts of South America in the fresh waters. The Chaca of Lake Baikal is found nowhere else; this is equally true of the Blindfish (*Amblyopsis*) of the Mammoth Cave, and of the *Proteus* of the caverns of Carinthia.

10. I beg not to be misunderstood. I do not impute to all naturalists the idea of ascribing all the differences or all the similarities of the organic world to climatic influences; I wish only to remind them that even the truest picture of the correlations of climate and geographical distribution, does not yet touch the question of origin, which is the point under consideration. Too little attention has thus far been paid to the facts bearing upon the peculiarities of structure of animals in connection with the range of their distribution. Such investigations are only beginning to be made, as native investigators are studying comparatively the anatomy of animals of different continents.

11. These remarks about the average size of animals in relation to their structure, cannot fail to meet with some objections, as it is well known, that under certain circumstances, man may modify the normal size of a variety of plants and of domesticated animals, and that even in their natural state occasional instances of extraordinary sizes occur. But this neither modifies the characteristic average, nor is it a case which has the least bearing upon the question of origin or even the maintenance of any species, but only upon individuals, respecting which more will be found in Sect. XVI. Moreover, it should not be

overlooked that there are limits to these variations, and that though animals and plants may be placed under influences conducive to a more or less voluminous growth, yet it is chiefly under the agency of man, that such changes reach their extremes. (See also Sect. XV.)

12. I trust no reader will be so ignorant of the facts here alluded to, as to infer from the use of the word "period" for different eras and epochs of great length, each of which is characterized by different animals, that the differences these animals exhibit, is in itself evidence of a change in the species. The question is, whether any changes take place during one or any of these periods. It is almost incredible how loosely some people will argue upon this point from a want of knowledge of the facts, even though they seem to reason logically. A distinguished physicist has recently taken up this subject of the immutability of species, and called in question the logic of those who uphold it. I will put his argument into as few words as possible, and show, I hope, that it does not touch the case. "Changes are observed from one geological period to another; species which do not exist at an earlier period are observed at a later period, while the former have disappeared; and though each species may have possessed its peculiarities unchanged for a lapse of time, the fact that when long periods are considered, all those of an earlier period are replaced by new ones at a later period, proves that species change in the end, provided a sufficiently long period of time is granted." I have nothing to object to the statement of facts, as far as it goes, but I maintain that the conclusion is not logical. It is true that species are limited to particular geological epochs; it is equally true that, in all geological formations, those of successive periods are different, one from the other. But because they so differ, does it follow that they have changed, and not been exchanged for, or replaced by others? The length of time taken for the operation has nothing to do with the argument. Granting myriads of years for each period, no matter how many or how few, the question remains simply this: When the change takes place, does it take place spontaneously, under the action of physical agents, according to their law, or is it produced by the intervention of an agency not in that way at work before or afterwards? A comparison may explain my view more fully. Let a lover of the fine arts visit a museum arranged systematically, and in which the works of the different schools are placed in chronological order; as he passes from one room to another, he beholds changes as great as those the palaeontologist observes in passing from one system of rocks to another. But because these works bear a closer resemblance as they belong to one or the other school, or to periods following one another closely, would the critic be in any way justified in assuming

that the earlier works have changed into those of a later period, or to deny that they are the works of artists living and active at the time of their production? The question about the immutability of species is identical with this supposed case. It is not because species have lasted for a longer or shorter time in past ages, that naturalists consider them as immutable, but because in the whole series of geological ages, taking the entire lapse of time which has passed since the first introduction of animals or plants upon earth, not the slightest evidence has yet been produced that species are actually transformed one into the other. We only know that they are different at different periods, as are works of art of different periods and of different schools; but as long as we have no other data to reason upon than those geology has furnished, to this day, it is as unphilosophical and illogical, because such differences exist, to assume that species do change, and have changed, that is, are transformed, or have been transformed, as it would be to maintain that works of art change in the course of time. We do not know how organized beings have originated, it is true; no naturalist can be prepared to account for their appearance in the beginning, or for their difference in different periods; but enough is known to repudiate the assumption of their transmutation, as it does not explain the facts, and shuts out further attempts at proper investigations.

13. Those who feel inclined to ascribe the differences which exist between species of different geological periods to the modifying influence of physical agents, and who look to the changes now going on among the living for the support of such an opinion, and may not be satisfied that the facts just mentioned are sufficient to prove the immutability of species, but may still believe that a longer period of time would yet do what thirty thousand years have not done, I beg leave to refer, for further consideration, to the charming song of Chamisso, entitled *Tragishe Geschichte*, and beginning as follows:

's war Einer dem's zu Herzen ging.

14. It might easily be shown that the exaggerated views generally entertained of the difference existing between man and monkeys, are traceable to the ignorance of the ancients, and especially the Greeks, to whom we owe chiefly our intellectual culture, of the existence of the Orang-Outang and the Chimpanzee. The animals most closely allied to man known to them were the Red Monkey, κῆβος, the Baboon, κυνοκέφαλος, and the Barbary Ape, πίθηκος. A modern translation of Aristotle, it is true, makes him say that monkeys form the transition between man and quadrupeds; (ARISTOTELES, Naturgeschichte der Thiere, von DR. F. STRACK, Frankfurt-am-Main, 1816,

p. 65;) but the original says no such thing. In the History of Animals, Book 2, Chap. V., we read only, ἔνια δὲ τῶν ζώων ἐπαμφοτερίζει τὴν φύσιν τῷ τε ἀνθρώπῳ καὶ τοῖς τετραποσιν. There is a wide difference between "partaking of the nature of both man and the quadrupeds," and "forming a transition between man and the quadrupeds." The whole chapter goes on enumerating the structural similarity of the three monkeys named above with man, but the idea of a close affinity is not even expressed, and still less that of a transition between man and the quadrupeds. The writer, on the contrary, dwells very fully upon the marked differences they exhibit, and knows as well as any modern anatomist has ever known, that monkeys have four hands. ἔχει δὲ καὶ βραχίονας, εσπῶρ ἄνθρωπος, . . . ἰδίους δὲ τοὺς πόδας. εἰσὶ γὰρ οἷον χεῖρες μεγάλαι. καὶ οἱ δάκτυλοι ὥσπερ οἱ τῶν χειρῶν, ὁ μέγας μακρότατος· καὶ τὸ κάτω τοῦ ποδὸς χειρὶ ὅμοιον, πλὴν ἐπὶ τὸ μῆκος τὸ τῆς χειρὸς ἐπὶ τα ἔσχατα τεῖνον καθάπερ θέναρ. Τοῦτο δὲ ἐπ' ἄκρου σκληρό-τερον, κακῶς καὶ ἀμυδρῶς μιμούμενον πτέρνην.

It is strange that these clear and precise distinctions should have been so entirely forgotten in the days of Linnaeus that the great reformer in Natural History had to confess, in the year 1746, that he knew no character by which to distinguish man from the monkeys. Fauna Suecica, Praefat. p. 2. "Nullum characterem adhuc eruere potui, unde homo a simia internoscatur." But it is not upon structural similarity or difference alone that the relations between man and animals have to be considered. The psychological history of animals shows that as man is related to animals by the plan of his structure, so are these related to him by the character of those very faculties which are so transcendent in man as to point at first to the necessity of disclaiming for him completely any relationship with the animal kingdom. Yet the natural history of animals is by no means completed after the somatic side of their nature has been thoroughly investigated; they, too, have a psychological individuality, which, though less fully studied, is nevertheless the connecting link between them and man. I cannot, therefore, agree with those authors who would disconnect mankind from the animal kingdom, and establish a distinct kingdom for man alone, as Ehrenberg (Das Naturreich des Menschen, Berlin, 1835, fol.) and lately I. Geoffroy St. Hilaire, (Hist. nat. générale, Paris, 1856, Tome 1, Part 2, p. 167) have done. Compare, also, Chap. II., where it is shown for every kind of groups of the animal kingdom that the amount of their difference one from the other never affords a sufficient ground for removing any of them into another category. A close study of the dog might satisfy every one of the similarity of his impulses with those of man, and those impulses are regulated in a manner which discloses psychical faculties in every respect of the same kind as those of man; moreover, he expresses by his voice his emotions and his feelings, with a precision which may be as intelligible to man as the articulated speech of his fellow men. His memory is so retentive that it frequently baffles that of man. And though all these faculties do not make a philosopher of him, they certainly place him in that respect upon a level with a considerable proportion of poor humanity. The intelligibility of the voice of animals to one another, and all their actions connected with such calls are also a strong argument of their perceptive power, and of their ability to act spontaneously and with logical sequence in accordance with these perceptions. There is a vast field open for investigation in the relations between the voice and the actions of animals, and a still more interesting subject of inquiry in the relationship between the cycle of intonations which different species of animals of the same family are capable of uttering, which, as far as I have as yet been able to trace them, stand to one another in the same relations as the different, so-called, families of languages (SCHLEGEL, (FR.,) Ueber die Sprache und Weisheit der Indier, Heidelberg, 1808, 1 vol. 8vo. —HUMBOLDT, (W., v.,) Ueber die Kawi-Sprache, auf der Insel Java, Berlin, 1836–39, 3 vols. 4to. Abh. Ak. d. Wissensch.—STEINTHAL, (H..) Grammatik, Logik und Psychologie, Berlin, 1855, 1 vol. 8vo.) in the human family. All the *Canina* bark; the howling of the wolves, the barking of the dogs and foxes, are only different modes of barking, comparable to one another in the same relation as the monosyllabic, the agglutinating, and the inflecting languages. The *Felidae* mew: the roaring of the lion is only another form of the mewing of our cats and the other species of the family. The *Equina* neigh or bray: the horse, the donkey, the zebra, the dow, do not differ much in the scale of their sounds. Our cattle, and the different kinds of wild bulls, have a similar affinity in their intonations; their lowing differs not in kind, but only in the mode of utterance. Among birds, this is, perhaps, still more striking. Who does not distinguish the note of any and every thrush, or of the warblers, the ducks, the fowls, etc., however numerous their species may be, and who can fail to perceive the affinity of their voices? And does this not indicate a similarity also in their mental faculties?

15. I say purposely, "in direct and immediate succession," as the phenomena of alternate generation are not included in metamorphosis, and consist chiefly in the production of new germs, which have their own metamorphosis; while metamorphosis proper relates only to the successive changes of one and the same germ.

II.

The Brazilian Journey

Note

The Nathaniel Thayer Expedition to Brazil left New York on April 1, 1865, bound for Rio de Janeiro. On the second day of the voyage Elizabeth Cary Agassiz wrote in "the common journal," which she and her husband kept of the expedition and which was published in 1867 as *A Journey in Brazil:*

April 2d, 1865.—Our first Sunday at sea. The weather is delicious, the ship as steady as anything on the water can be, and even the most forlorn of our party have little excuse for sea-sickness. We have had service from Bishop Potter this morning, and since then we have been on deck reading, walking, watching a singular cloud, which the captain says is a cloud of smoke, in the direction of Petersburg. We think it may be the smoke of a great decisive engagement going on while we sail peacefully along. . . . Mr. Agassiz is busy to-day in taking notes, at regular intervals, of the temperature of the water, as we approach the Gulf Stream.

The "singular cloud" was the torrential battle of Fort Gregg, on the eve of the storming of Petersburg, Virginia, and the final agony of the Civil War. The juxtaposition of this awful moment and the ship-load of scientists sailing within sight of its cannon smoke symbolizes perfectly the pure isolation of Agassiz's science. Never again would the scientist be disengaged from the brutalities of war, nor would wars be fought by armies alone. Agassiz had become an American citizen just before the war, to emphasize his faith in the stability of the Union, and to declare an intellectual declaration of independence for the American scientist, urging him not to publish his work abroad, but to demand the attention of Europe to American science, the organization of which was in large part his inspiration. The war found Agassiz embarrassed, as he had deep sympathies with the South, and could not insult the fine courtesies which Southern naturalists had paid him. The Brazilian expedition was partly a polite bowing out of the war years, as well as a vacation. It is typical of Agassiz that his vacation from overwork should take the form of what he considered a ramble over the territories which Humboldt had first studied. Agassiz knew that he "could make slight use of the opportunities I should have; and though the expedition might be a pleasant one for myself, it would have no important result for science." Had he the means, however, it was clear that the expedition could bring the collection in the university museum to "a level with the first institutions of the kind." He had asked for so much for the museum, and had obtained, first from the bequest of F. C. Gray, fifty thousand dollars, then seventy thousand dollars, raised by "a committee of gentlemen," and a hundred thousand from the state of Massachusetts. But before the expedition he was approached by Nathaniel Thayer. "You wish, of course," he said to Agassiz, "to give it a scientific character; take six assistants with you, and I will be responsible for all their expenses, personal and scientific."

Two chapters of the *Journal* are reproduced here. It should be pointed out that the passages concerning glaciers are now known to be an error; the reader can find a full discussion of this matter in Chapter 9 of Edward Lurie's *Louis Agassiz: A Life in Science* (1960).

II. The Brazilian Journey

CHAPTER XIII.

Physical History of the Amazons.

A few days before we left Para, Senhor Pimenta Bueno invited his friends and acquaintances, who had expressed a wish to hear Mr. Agassiz's views on the geological character of the Amazonian Valley, to meet at his house in the evening for that purpose. The guests were some two hundred in number, and the whole affair was very unceremonious, assuming rather the character of a meeting for conversation or discussion than that of an audience collected to hear a studied address. The substance of this talk or lecture, as subsequently written out by Mr. Agassiz, afterward appeared in the Atlantic Monthly, and is inserted here, with some few alterations under the head of a separate chapter. The reader will find occasional repetitions of facts already stated in the earlier part of the narrative; but they are retained for the sake of giving a complete and consistent review of the subject at this point of our journey, where it became possible to compare the geological structure of the Amazonian Valley with that of the southern provinces of Brazil and of those bordering on the Atlantic coast.

The existence of a glacial period, however much derided when first announced, is now a recognized fact. The divergence of opinion respecting it is limited to a question of extent; and after my recent journey in the Amazons, I am led to add a new chapter to the strange history of glacial phenomena, taken from the southern hemisphere, and even from the tropics themselves.

I am prepared to find that the statement of this new phase of the glacial period will awaken among my scientific colleagues an opposition even more violent than that by which the first announcement of my views on this subject was met. I am, however, willing to bide my time; feeling sure that, as the theory of the ancient extension of glaciers in Europe has gradually come to be accepted by geologists, so will the existence of like phenomena, both in North and South America, during the same epoch, be recognized sooner or later as part of a great series of physical events extending over the whole globe. Indeed, when the ice-period is fully understood, it will be seen that the absurdity lies in supposing that climatic conditions so different could be limited to a small portion of the world's surface. If the geological winter existed at all, it must have been cosmic; and it is quite as rational to look for its traces in the Western as in the Eastern hemisphere, to the south of the equator as to the north of it. Impressed by this wider view of the subject, confirmed by a number of unpublished investigations which I have made during the last three or four years in the United States, I came to South America, expecting to find in the tropical regions new evidences of a bygone glacial period, though, of course, under different aspects. Such a result seemed to me the logical sequence of what I had already observed in Europe and in North America.

On my arrival in Rio de Janeiro—the port at which I first landed in Brazil—my attention was immediately attracted by a very peculiar formation consisting of an ochraceous, highly ferruginous, sandy clay. During a stay of three months in Rio, whence I made many excursions into the neighboring country, I had opportunities of studying this deposit, both in the province of Rio de Janeiro and in the adjoining province of Minas Geraes. I found that it rested everywhere upon the undulating surfaces of the solid rocks in place, was almost entirely destitute of stratification, and contained a variety of pebbles and boulders. The pebbles were chiefly quartz, sometimes scattered indiscriminately throughout the deposit, sometimes lying in a seam between it and the rock below; while the boulders were either sunk in its mass, or resting loosely on the surface. At Tizuca, a few miles out of the city of Rio, among the picturesque hills lying to the southwest of it, these phenomena may be seen in great perfection. Near

Bennett's Hotel there are a great number of erratic boulders, having no connection whatever with the rock in place; and also a bluff of this superficial deposit studded with boulders, resting above the partially stratified metamorphic rock. Other excellent opportunites for observing this formation, also within easy reach from the city, are afforded along the whole line of the Dom Pedro Segundo Railroad, where the cuts expose admirable sections, showing the red, unstratified, homogeneous mass of sandy clay resting above the solid rock, and often divided from it by a thin bed of pebbles. There can be no doubt, in the mind of any one familiar with similar facts observed in other parts of the world, that this is one of the many forms of drift connected with glacial action. I was, however, far from anticipating, when I first met it in the neighborhood of Rio, that I should afterwards find it spreading over the surface of the country from north to south and from east to west, with a continuity which gives legible connection to the whole geological history of the continent.

It is true that the extensive decomposition of the underlying rock, penetrating sometimes to a considerable depth, makes it often difficult to distinguish between it and the drift; and the problem is made still more puzzling by the fact that the surface of the drift, when baked by exposure to the hot sun, often assumes the appearance of decomposed rock, so that great care is required for a correct interpretation of the facts. A little practice, however, trains the eye to read these appearances aright; and I may say that I have learned to recognize everywhere the limit between the two formations. There is indeed one safe guide, namely, the undulating line, reminding one of *roches moutonnées*,[1] and marking the irregular surface of the rock on which the drift was accumulated; whatever modifications the one or the other may have undergone, this line seems never to disappear. Another deceptive feature, arising from the frequent disintegration of the rocks and from the brittle character of some of them, is the presence of loose fragments, which simulate erratic boulders, but are in fact only detached masses of the rock in place. A careful examination of their structure, however, will at

[Footnotes for Part II will be found on page 169.]

once show the geologist whether they belong where they are found, or have been brought from a distance to their present resting-place.

But, while the features to which I have alluded are unquestionably drift phenomena, they present in their wider extension, and especially in the northern part of Brazil, some phases of glacial action hitherto unobserved. Just as the investigation of the ice-period in the United States has shown us that ice-fields may move over open level plains, as well as along the slopes of mountain valleys, so does a study of the same class of facts in South America reveal new and unlooked-for features in the history of the ice-period. Some will say that the fact of the advance of ice-fields over an open country is by no means established, inasmuch as many geologists believe all the so-called glacial traces— viz., striae, furrows, polish, etc., found in the United States—to have been made by floating icebergs at a time when the continent was submerged. To this I can only answer that, in the State of Maine, I have followed, compass in hand, the same set of furrows, running from north to south in one unvarying line, over a surface of one hundred and thirty miles, from the Katahdin Iron Range to the seashore. These furrows follow all the inequalities of the country, ascending ranges of hills varying from twelve to fifteen hundred feet in height, and descending into the intervening valleys only two or three hundred feet above the sea, or sometimes even on a level with it. I take it to be impossible that a floating mass of ice should travel onward in one rectilinear direction, turning neither to the right nor to the left, for such a distance. Equally impossible would it be for a detached mass of ice, swimming on the surface of the water, or even with its base sunk considerably below it, to furrow in a straight line the summits and sides of the hills, and the bottoms of the intervening valleys. It would be carried over the inequalities of the country without touching the lowest depressions. Instead of ascending the mountains, it would remain stranded against any elevation which rose greatly above its own base, and, if caught between two parallel ridges, would float up and down between them. Moreover, the action of solid, unbroken ice, moving over the ground in immediate contact with it, is so different from that of

floating ice-rafts or icebergs that, though the latter have unquestionably dropped erratic boulders, and made furrows and
striae on the surface where they happened to be grounded, these
phenomena will easily be distinguished from the more connected
tracks of glaciers, or extensive sheets of ice, resting directly upon
the face of the country and advancing over it.

There seems thus far to be an inextricable confusion in the
ideas of many geologists as to the respective action of currents,
icebergs, and glaciers. It is time that they should learn to distinguish between classes of facts so different from each other,
and so easily recognized after the discrimination has once been
made. As to the southward movement of an immense field of ice,
extending over the whole North, it seems inevitable, the moment
we admit that snow may accumulate around the pole in such
quantities as to initiate a pressure radiating in every direction.
Snow, alternately thawing and freezing, must, like water, find
its level at last. A sheet of snow ten or fifteen thousand feet in
thickness, extending all over the northern and southern portions
of the globe, must necessarily lead, in the end, to the formation
of a northern and southern cap of ice, moving toward the equator.

I have spoken of Tijuca and the Dom Pedro Railroad as favorable localities for studying the peculiar southern drift; but
one meets it in every direction. A sheet of drift, consisting of the
same homogeneous, unstratified paste, and containing loose materials of all sorts and sizes, covers the country. It is of very uneven
thickness—sometimes thrown into relief, as it were, by the surrounding denudations, and rising into hills; sometimes reduced
to a thin layer; sometimes, as, for instance, on steep slopes,
washed entirely away, leaving the bare face of the rock exposed.
It has, however, remained comparatively undisturbed on some
very abrupt ascents; as may be seen on the Corcovado, along the
path leading up the mountain, where there are some very fine
banks of drift, the more striking from the contrast of their deep-
red color with the surrounding vegetation. I have myself followed this sheet of drift from Rio de Janeiro to the top of the
Serra do Mar, where, just outside the pretty town of Petropolis,
the river Piabanha may be seen flowing between banks of drift,

in which it has excavated its bed; thence I have traced it along the beautiful macadamized road leading to Juiz de Fora in the province of Minas Geraes, and beyond this to the farther side of the Serra da Babylonia. Throughout this whole tract of country the drift may be seen along the roadside, in immediate contact with the native crystalline rock. The fertility of the land, also, is a guide to the presence of drift. Wherever it lies thickest over the surface, there are the most flourishing coffee-plantations; and I believe that a more systematic regard to this fact would have a most beneficial influence upon the agricultural interests of the country. No doubt the fertility arises from the great variety of chemical elements contained in the drift, and the kneading process it has undergone beneath the gigantic ice-plough—a process which makes glacial drift everywhere the most fertile soil. Since my return from the Amazons, my impression as to the general distribution of these phenomena has been confirmed by the reports of some of my assistants, who have been travelling in other parts of the country. Mr. Frederick C. Hartt, accompanied by Mr. Copeland, one of the volunteer aids of the expedition, has been making collections and geological observations in the province of Spiritu Santo, in the valley of the Rio Doce, and afterwards in the valley of the Mucury. He informs me that he has found everywhere the same sheet of red, unstratified clay, with pebbles, and occasional boulders overlying the rock in place. Mr. Orestes St. John, who, taking the road through the interior, has visited, with the same objects in view, the valleys of the Rio San Francisco and the Rio das Velhas, and also the valley of Piauhy, gives the same account, with the exception that he found no erratic boulders in these more northern regions. The rarity of erratic boulders, not only in the deposits of the Amazons proper, but in those of the whole region which may be considered as the Amazonian basin, is accounted for, as we shall see hereafter, by the mode of their formation. The observations of Mr. Hartt and Mr. St. John are the more valuable, because I had employed them both, on our first arrival in Rio, in making geological surveys of different sections on the Dom Pedro Railroad, so that they had a great familiarity with those formations before starting on their separate journeys. Recently, Mr. St. John and myself met in

Para on our return from our respective explorations, and I have had an opportunity of comparing on the spot his geological sections from the valley of the Piauhy with the Amazonian deposits. There can be no doubt of the absolute identity of the formations in these valleys.

Having arranged the work of my assistants, and sent several of them to collect and make geological examinations in other directions, I myself, with the rest of my companions, proceeded up the coast to Para. I was surprised to find at every step of my progress the same geological phenomena which had met me at Rio. It was my friend, Major Coutinho, already an experienced Amazonian traveller, who first told me that this formation continued through the whole valley of the Amazons, and was also to be found on all of its affluents which he had visited, although he had never thought of referring it to so recent a period. And here let me say that the facts I now state are by no means exclusively the result of my own investigations. They are in great part due to Major Coutinho, a member of the Brazilian government corps of engineers, who, by the kindness of the Emperor, was associated with me in my Amazonian expedition. I can truly say that he has been my good genius throughout the whole journey, saving me, by his previous knowledge of the ground, from the futile and misdirected expenditure of means and time often inevitable in a new country, where one is imperfectly acquainted both with the people and their language. We have worked together in this investigation; my only advantage over him being my greater familiarity with like phenomena in Europe and North America, and consequent readiness in the practical handling of the facts and in perceiving their connection. Major Coutinho's assertion, that on the banks of the Amazons I should find the same red, unstratified clay as in Rio and along the southern coast, seemed to me at first almost incredible, impressed as I was with the generally received notions as to the ancient character of the Amazonian deposits, referred by Humboldt to the Devonian, and by Martius to the Triassic period, and considered by all travellers to be at least as old as the Tertiaries. The result, however, confirmed his report, at least so far as the component materials of the formation are concerned; but, as will be seen hereafter, the mode of their deposition, and the time at which it took place, have not been the same at the north and south; and this difference of circumstances had modified the aspect of a formation essentially the same throughout. At first sight, it would indeed appear that this formation, as it exists in the valley of the Amazons, is identical with that of Rio; but it differs from it in the rarity of its boulders, and in showing occasional signs of stratification. It is also everywhere underlaid by coarse, well-stratified deposits, resembling somewhat the *Recife* of Bahia and Pernambuco; whereas the unstratified drift of the south rests immediately upon the undulating surface of whatever rock happens to make the foundation of the country, whether stratified or crystalline. The peculiar sandstone on which the Amazonian clay rests exists nowhere else. Before proceeding, however, to describe the Amazonian deposits in detail, I ought to say something of the nature and origin of the valley itself.

The valley of the Amazons was first sketched out by the elevation of two tracts of land; namely, the plateau of Guiana on the north, and the central plateau of Brazil on the south. It is probable that, at the time these two table-lands were lifted above the sea-level, the Andes did not exist, and the ocean flowed between them through an open strait. It would seem (and this is a curious result of modern geological investigations) that the portions of the earth's surface earliest raised above the ocean have trended from east to west. The first tract of land lifted above the waters in North America was also a long continental island, running from Newfoundland almost to the present base of the Rocky Mountains. This tendency may be attributed to various causes—to the rotation of the earth, the consequent depression of its poles, and the breaking of its crust along the lines of greatest tension thus produced. At a later period, the upheaval of the Andes took place, closing the western side of this strait, and thus transforming it into a gulf, open only toward the east. Little or nothing is known of the earlier stratified deposits resting against the crystalline masses first uplifted along the borders of the Amazonian Valley. There is here no sequence, as in North America, of Azoic, Silurian, Devonian, and in Carboniferous formations, shored up against each other by the gradual upheaval

of the continent; although, unquestionably, older palaeozoic
and secondary beds underlie, here and there, the later formations. Indeed, Major Coutinho has found palaeozoic deposits,
with characteristic Brachiopods, in the valley of the Rio Tapajos,
at the first cascade, and carboniferous deposits have been noticed
along the Rio Guapore and the Rio Mamore. But the first chapter
in the valley's geological history about which we have connected
and trustworthy data is that of the cretaceous period. It seems
certain, that, at the close of the secondary age, the whole Amazonian basin became lined with a cretaceous deposit, the margins of which crop out at various localities on its borders. They
have been observed along its southern limits, on its western out-
skirts along the Andes, in Venezuela along the shore-line of
mountains, and also in certain localities near its eastern edge. I
well remember that one of the first things which awakened my
interest in the geology of the Amazonian Valley was the sight of
some cretaceous fossil fishes from the province of Ceara. These
fossil fishes were collected by Mr. George Gardner, to whom
science is indebted for the most extensive information yet obtained respecting the geology of that part of Brazil. In this connection, let me say that I shall speak of the provinces of Ceara,
Piauhy, and Maranham as belonging geologically to the valley of
the Amazons, though their shore is bathed by the ocean and
their rivers empty directly into the Atlantic. But I entertain no
doubt that, at an earlier period, the northeastern coast of Brazil
stretched much farther seaward than in our day; so far, indeed,
that in those times the rivers of all these provinces must have
been tributaries of the Amazons in its eastward course. The evidence for this conclusion is substantially derived from the identity of the deposits in the valleys belonging to these provinces
with those of the valleys through which the actual tributaries of
the Amazons flow; as for instance, the Tocantins, the Xingu, the
Tapajos, the Madeira, etc. Besides the fossils above alluded to
from the eastern borders of this ancient basin, I have had recently another evidence of its cretaceous character from its southern region. Mr. William Chandless, on his return from a late journey on the Rio Purus, presented me with a series of fossil remains
of the highest interest, and undoubtedly belonging to the creta-

ceous period. They were collected by himself on the Rio Aquiry, an affluent of the Rio Purus. Most of them were found in place between the tenth and eleventh degrees of south latitude, and the sixty-seventh and sixty-ninth degrees of west longitude from Greenwich, in localities varying from four hundred and thirty to six hundred and fifty feet above the sea-level. There are among them remains of Mosasaurus, and of fishes closely allied to those already represented by Faujas in his description of Maestricht, and characteristic, as is well known to geological students, of the most recent cretaceous period.

Thus in its main features the valley of the Amazons, like that of the Mississippi, is a cretaceous basin. This resemblance suggests a further comparison between the twin continents of North and South America. Not only is their general form the same, but their framework, as we may call it—that is, the lay of their great mountain-chains and of their table-lands, with the extensive intervening depressions—presents a striking similarity. Indeed, a zoologist, accustomed to trace a like structure under variously modified animal forms, cannot but have his homological studies recalled to his mind by the coincidence between certain physical features in the northern and southern parts of the Western hemisphere. And yet here, as throughout all nature, these correspondences are combined with a distinctness of individualization which leaves its respective character, not only to each continent as a whole, but also to the different regions circumscribed within its borders. In both, however, the highest mountain-chains, the Rocky Mountains and the Western Coast Range, with their wide intervening table-land in North America, and the chain of the Andes, with its lesser plateaux in South America, run along the western coast; both have a great eastern promontory, Newfoundland in the Northern continent, and Cape St. Roque in the Southern: and though the resemblance between the inland elevations is perhaps less striking, yet the Canadian range, the White Mountains, and the Alleghanies may very fairly be compared to the table-lands of Guiana and Brazil, and the Serra do Mar. Similar correspondences may be traced among the river-systems. The Amazons and the St. Lawrence, though so different in dimensions, remind us of each other by their trend and geographical position; and while the one is fed by the largest river-system in the world, the other drains the most extensive lake surfaces known to exist in immediate contiguity. The Orinoco, with its bay, recalls Hudson's Bay and its many tributaries, and the Rio Magdalena may be said to be the South-American Mackenzie; while the Rio de la Plata represents geographically our Mississippi, and the Paraguay recalls the Missouri. The Parana may be compared to the Ohio; the Pilcomayo, Vermejo, and Salado rivers, to the river Platte, the Arkansas, and the Red River in the United States; while the rivers farther south, emptying into the Gulf of Mexico, represent the rivers of Patagonia and the southern parts of the Argentine Republic. Not only is there this general correspondence between the mountain elevations and the river-systems, but as the larger river-basins of North America —those of the St. Lawrence, the Mississippi, and the Mackenzie —meet in the low tracts extending along the foot of the Rocky Mountains, so do the basins of the Amazons, the Rio de la Plata, and the Orinoco join each other along the eastern slope of the Andes.

But while in geographical homology the Amazons compares with the St. Lawrence, and the Mississippi with the Rio de la Plata, the Mississippi and the Amazons, as has been said, resemble each other in their local geological character. They have both received a substratum of cretaceous beds, above which are accumulated more recent deposits, so that, in their most prominent geological features, both may be considered as cretaceous basins, containing extensive deposits of a very recent age. Of the history of the Amazonian Valley during the periods immediately following the Cretaceous, we know little or nothing. Whether the Tertiary deposits are hidden under the more modern ones; or whether they are wholly wanting, the basin having, perhaps, been raised above the sea-level before that time; or whether they have been swept away by the tremendous inundations in the valley, which have certainly destroyed a great part of the cretaceous deposit—they have never been observed in any part of the Amazonian basin. Whatever Tertiary deposits are represented in

geological maps of this region are so marked in consequence of
an incorrect identification of straits belonging, in fact, to a much
more recent period.

A minute and extensive survey of the valley of the Amazons
is by no means an easy task, and its difficulty is greatly increased
by the fact that the lower formations are only accessible on the
river margins during the *vasante*, or dry season, when the waters
shrink in their beds, leaving a great part of their banks exposed.
It happened that the first three or four months of my journey
(August, September, October and November) were those when
the waters are lowest—reaching their minimum in September
and October, and beginning to rise again in November—so that
I had an excellent opportunity, in ascending the river, of observing its geological structure. Throughout its whole length, three
distinct geological formations may be traced, the two lower of
which have followed in immediate succession, and are conformable with one another, while the third rests unconformably
upon them, following all the inequalities of the greatly denudated
surface presented by the second formation. Notwithstanding this
seeming interruption in the sequence of these deposits, the third,
as we shall presently see, belongs to the same series, and was accumulated in the same basin. The lowest set of beds of the whole
series is rarely visible; but it seems everywhere to consist of sandstone, or even of loose sands well stratified, the coarser materials
lying invariably below, and the finer above. Upon this lower set
of beds rests everywhere an extensive deposit of fine laminated
clays, varying in thickness, but frequently dividing into layers as
thin as a sheet of paper. In some localities they exhibit, in
patches, an extraordinary variety of beautiful colors—pink,
orange, crimson, yellow, gray, blue, and also black and white. It
is from these beds that the Indians prepare their paints. These
clay deposits assume occasionally a peculiar appearance, and one
which might mislead the observer as to their true nature. When
their surface has been long exposed to the action of the atmosphere and to the heat of the burning sun, they look so much like
clay-slates of the oldest geological epochs that, at first sight, I
took them for primary slates, my attention being attracted to
them by a regular cleavage as distinct as that of the most ancient

clay-slates. And yet at Tonantins, on the banks of the Solimoens, in a locality where their exposed surfaces had this primordial appearance, I found in these very beds a considerable amount of well-preserved leaves, the character of which proves their recent origin. These leaves do not even indicate as ancient a period as the Tertiaries, but resemble so closely the vegetation of to-day that I have no doubt, when examined by competent authority, they will be identified with living plants. The presence of such an extensive clay formation, stretching over a surface of more than three thousand miles in length and about seven hundred in breadth, is not easily explained under any ordinary circumstances. The fact that it is so thoroughly laminated shows that, in the basin in which it was formed, the waters must have been unusually quiet, containing identical materials throughout, and that these materials must have been deposited over the whole bottom in the same way. It is usually separated from the superincumbent beds by a glazed crust of hard, compact sandstone, almost resembling a ferruginous quartzite.

Upon this follow beds of sand and sandstone, varying in the regularity of their strata, reddish in color, often highly ferruginous, and more or less nodulous or porous. They present frequent traces of cross-stratification, alternating with regularly stratified horizontal beds, with here and there an intervening layer of clay. It would seem as if the character of the water-basin had now changed, and as if the waters under which this second formation was deposited had vibrated between storm and calm, had sometimes flowed more gently, and again had been tossed to and fro, giving to some of the beds the aspect of true torrential deposits. Indeed, these sandstone formations present a great variety of aspects. Sometimes they are very regularly laminated, or assume even the appearance of the hardest quartzite. This is usually the case with the uppermost beds. In other localities, and more especially in the lowermost beds, the whole mass is honeycombed, as if drilled by worms or boring shells, the hard parts enclosing softer sands or clays. Occasionally the ferruginous materials prevail to such an extent that some of these beds might be mistaken for bog-ore, while others contain a large amount of clay, more regularly stratified, and alternating with strata of sandstone, thus recalling the most characteristic forms of the Old Red or Triassic formations. This resemblance has, no doubt, led to the identification of the Amazonian deposits with the more ancient formations of Europe. At Monte Alegre, of which I shall presently speak more in detail, such a clay bed divides the lower from the upper sandstone. The thickness of these sandstones is extremely variable. In the basin of the Amazons proper, they hardly rise anywhere above the level of high water during the rainy season; while at low water, in the summer months, they may be observed everywhere along the river-banks. It will be seen, however, that the limit between high and low water gives no true measure of the original thickness of the whole series.

In the neighborhood of Almeyrim, at a short distance from the northern bank of the river, and nearly parallel with its course, there rises a line of low hills, interrupted here and there, but extending in evident connection from Almeyrim through the region of Monte Alegre to the heights of Obydos. These hills have attracted the attention of travellers, not only from their height, which appears greater than it is, because they rise abruptly from an extensive plain, but also on account of their curious form; many of them being perfectly level on top, like smooth tables, and very abruptly divided from each other by low, intervening spaces. Nothing has hitherto been known of the geological structure of these hills, but they have been usually represented as the southernmost spurs of the table-land of Guiana. On ascending the river, I felt the greatest curiosity to examine them; but at the time I was deeply engrossed in studying the distribution of fishes in the Amazonian waters, and in making large ichthyological collections, for which it was very important not to miss the season of low water, when the fishes are most easily obtained. I was, therefore, obliged to leave this most interesting geological problem, and content myself with examining the structure of the valley so far as it could be seen on the river-banks and in the neighborhood of my different collecting stations. On my return, however, when my collections were completed, I was free to pursue this investigation, in which Major Coutinho was as much interested as myself. We determined to select Monte Alegre as the centre of our exploration, the serra in that region being higher than elsewhere.

As I was detained by indisposition at Manaos for some days at the time we had appointed for the excursion, Major Coutinho preceded me, and had already made one trip to the serra, with some very interesting results, when I joined him, and we took a second journey together. Monte Alegre lies on a side arm of the Amazons, a little off from its main course. This side arm, called the Rio Gurupatuba, is simply a channel, running parallel with the Amazons, and cutting through from a higher to a lower point. Its dimensions are, however, greatly exaggerated in all the maps thus far published, where it is usually made to appear as a considerable northern tributary of the Amazons. The town stands on an elevated terrace, separated from the main stream by the Rio Gurupatuba and by an extensive flat, consisting of numerous lakes divided from each other by low, alluvial land, and mostly connected by narrow channels. To the west of the town this terrace sinks abruptly to a wide sandy plain called the Campos, covered with a low forest-growth, and bordered on its farther limit by the picturesque serra of Erere. The form of this mountain is so abrupt, its rise from the plains so bold and sudden, that it seems more than twice its real height. Judging by the eye and comparing it with the mountains I had last seen—the Corcovado, the Gavia, and Tijuca range in the neighborhood of Rio—I had supposed it to be three or four thousand feet high, and was greatly astonished when our barometric observations showed it to be somewhat less than nine hundred feet in its most elevated point. This, however, agrees with Martius's measurement of the Almeyrim hills, which he says are eight hundred feet in height.

We passed three days in the investigation of the Serra of Erere, and found it to consist wholly of the sandstone deposits already described, and to have exactly the same geological constitution. In short, the Serra of Monte Alegre, and of course all those connected with it on the northern side of the river, lie in the prolongation of the lower beds forming the banks of the river, their greater height being due simply to the fact that they have not been worn to the same low level. The opposite range of Santarem, which has the same general outline and character, shares, no doubt, the same geological structure. In one word, all these hills were formerly part of a continuous formation, and owe their present outline and their isolated position to a colossal denudation. The surface of the once unbroken strata, which in their original condition must have formed an immense plain covered by water, has been cut into ravines or carried away over large tracts, to a greater or less depth, leaving only such portions standing as, from their hardness, could resist the floods which swept over it. The longitudinal trend of these hills is to be ascribed to the direction of the current which caused the denudation, while their level summits are due to the regularity of the stratification. They are not all table-topped, however; among them are many of smaller size, in which the sides have been gradually worn down, producing a gently rounded surface. Of course, under the heavy tropical rains this denudation is still going on, though in a greatly modified form.

I cannot speak of this Serra without alluding to the great beauty and extraordinary extent of the view to be obtained from it. Indeed, it was here that for the first time the geography of the country presented itself to my mind as a living reality in all its completeness. Insignificant as is its actual height, the Serra of Erere commands a wider prospect than is to be had from many a more imposing mountain; for the surrounding plain, covered with forests and ploughed by countless rivers, stretches away for hundreds of leagues in every direction, without any object to obstruct the view. Standing on the brow of the Serra, with the numerous lakes intersecting the lowlands at its base, you look across the valley of the Amazons, as far as the eye can reach, and through its centre you follow for miles on either side the broad flood of the great river, carrying its yellow waters to the sea. As I stood there, panoramas from the Swiss mountains came up to my memory, and I fancied myself on the Alps, looking across the plain of Switzerland instead of the bed of the Amazons; the distant line of the Santarem hills on the southern bank of the river, and lower than the northern chain, representing the Jura range. As if to complete the comparison, Alpine lichens were growing among the cacti and palms, and a crust of Arctic cryptogamous growth covered rocks, between which sprang tropical flowers. On the northern flank of this Serra I found the only genuine erratic boulders I have seen in the whole length of the Amazonian Val-

ley from Para to the frontier of Peru, though there are many detached masses of rock, as, for instance, at Pedreira, near the junction of the Rio Negro and Rio Branco, which might be mistaken
for them, but are due to the decomposition of the rocks in place.
The boulders of Erere are entirely distinct from the rock of the
Serra, and consist of masses of compact horn-blende.

It would seem that these two ranges skirting a part of the
northern and southern banks of the Lower Amazons are not the
only remnants of this arenaceous formation in its primitive altitude. On the banks of the Rio Japura, in the Serra of Cupati,
Major Coutinho has found the same beds rising to the same
height. It thus appears, by positive evidence, that over an extent
of a thousand miles these deposits had a very considerable thickness, in the present direction of the valley. How far they extended
in width has not been ascertained by direct observation; for we
have not seen how they sink away to the northward, and towards
the south the denudation has been so complete that, except in the
very low range of hills in the neighborhood of Santarem, they do
not rise above the plain. But the fact that this formation once had
a thickness of more than eight hundred feet within the limits
where we have had an opportunity of observing it, leaves no
doubt that it must have extended to the edge of the basin, filling
it to the same height throughout its whole extent. The thickness
of the deposits gives a measure for the colossal scale of the denudations by which this immense accumulation was reduced to
its present level. Here, then, is a system of high hills, having the
prominence of mountains in the landscape, produced by causes
to whose agency inequalities on the earth's surface of this magni-
tude have never yet been ascribed. We may fairly call them denudation mountains.

At this stage of the inquiry we have to account for two remarkable phenomena—first, the filling of the Amazonian bottom
with coarse arenaceous materials and finely laminated clays, immediately followed by sandstones rising to a height of more than
eight hundred feet above the sea, the basin meanwhile having no
rocky barrier towards the ocean on its eastern side; secondly, the
wearing away and reduction of these formations to their present
level by a denudation more extensive than any thus far recorded

in the annals of geology, which has given rise to all the most prominent hills and mountain-chains along the northern bank of the river. Before seeking an explanation of these facts, let us look at the third and uppermost deposit.

This deposit is essentially the same as the Rio drift; but in the north it presents itself under a somewhat different aspect. As in Rio, it is a clayey deposit, containing more or less sand, and reddish in color, though varying from deep ochre to a brownish tint. It is not so absolutely destitute of stratification here as in its more southern range, though the traces of stratification are rare, and, when they do occur, are faint and indistinct. The materials are also more completely comminuted, and, as I said above, contain hardly any large masses, though quartz pebbles are sometimes scattered throughout the deposit, and occasionally a thin seam of pebbles, exactly as in the Rio drift, is seen resting between it and the underlying sandstone. In some places this bed of pebbles intersects even the mass of the clay, giving it, in such instances, an unquestionably stratified character. There can be no doubt that this more recent formation rests unconformably upon the sandstone beds beneath it; for it fills all the inequalities of their denudated surfaces, whether they be more or less limited furrows, or wide, undulating depressions. It may be seen everywhere along the banks of the river, above the stratified sandstone, sometimes with the river-mud accumulated against it; at the season of the *enchente,* or high water, it is the only formation left exposed above the water-level. Its thickness is not great; it varies from twenty or thirty to fifty feet, and may occasionally rise nearly to a hundred feet in height, though this is rarely the case. It is evident that this formation also was once continuous, stretching over the whole basin at one level. Though it is now worn down in many places, and has wholly disappeared in others, its connection may be readily traced; since it is everywhere visible, not only on opposite banks of the Amazons, but also on those of all its tributaries, as far as their shores have been examined. I have said that it rests always above the sandstone beds. This is true, with one exception. Wherever the sandstone deposits retain their original thickness, as in the hills of Monte Alegre and Almeyrim, the red clay is not found on their summits, but occurs only in their ravines and hollows, or resting against their sides. This shows that it is not only posterior to the sandstone, but was accumulated in a shallower basin, and consequently never reached so high a level. The boulders of Erere do not rest on the stratified sandstone of the Serra, but are sunk in the unstratified mass of the clay. This should be remembered, as it will presently be seen that their position associates them with a later period than that of the mountain itself. The unconformability of the ochraceous clay and the underlying sandstones might lead to the idea that the two formations belong to distinct geological periods, and are not due to the same agency acting at successive times. One feature, however, shows their close connection. The ochraceous clay exhibits a remarkable identity of configuration with the underlying sandstones. An extensive survey of the two, in their mutual relations, shows clearly that they were both deposited by the same water-system within the same basin, but at different levels. Here and there the clay formation has so pale and grayish a tint that it may be confounded with the mud deposits of the river. These latter, however, never rise so high as the ochraceous clay, but are everywhere confined within the limits of high and low water. The islands also, in the main course of the Amazons, consist invariably of river-mud; while those portions of the land by diverging branches of the main stream always consist of the well-known sandstones, capped by the ochre-colored clay.

It may be truly said that there does not exist on the surface of the earth a formation known to geologists resembling that of the Amazons. Its extent is stupendous; it stretches from the Atlantic shore, through the whole width of Brazil, into Peru, to the very foot of the Andes. Humboldt speaks of it "in the vast plains of the Amazons, in the eastern boundary of Jaen de Bracamoros," and says, "This prodigious extension of red sandstone in the low grounds stretching along the east of the Andes is one of the most striking phenomena I observed during my examination of rocks in the equinoctial regions." [2] When the great natural philosopher wrote these lines, he had no idea how much these deposits extended beyond the field of his observations. Indeed, they are not limited to the main bed of the Amazons; they have been followed along the banks of its tributaries to the south and north as far as these have been ascended. They occur on the margins of the Huallaga and the Ucayale, on those of the Ica, the Hyutahy, the Hyurua, the Hyapura, and the Purus. On the banks of the Hyapura, where Major Coutinho has traced them, they are found as far as the Cataract of Cupati. I have followed them along the Rio Negro to its junction with the Rio Branco; and Humboldt not only describes them from a higher point on this same river, but also from the valley of the Orinoco. Finally, they may be tracked along the banks of the Madeira, the Tapajos, the Xingu, and the Tocantins, as well as on the shores of the Guatuma, the Trombetas, and other northern affluents of the Amazons. The observations of Martius, those of Gardner, and the recent survey above alluded to, made by my assistant, Mr. St. John, of the valley of the Rio Guruguea and that of the Rio Paranahyba, show that the great basin of Piauhy is also identical in its geological structure with the lateral valleys of the Amazons. The same is true of the large island of Marajo, lying at the mouth of the Amazons. And yet I believe that even this does not cover the whole ground, and that some future writer may say of my estimate, as I have said of Humboldt's, that it falls short of the truth; for, if my generalizations are correct, the same formation will be found extending over the whole basin of the Paraguay and the Rio de la Plata, and along their tributaries, to the very heart of the Andes.

Such are the facts. The question now arises, How were these vast deposits formed? The easiest answer, and the one which most readily suggests itself, is that of a submersion of the continent at successive periods, to allow the accumulation of these materials, and its subsequent elevation. I reject this explanation for this simple reason that the deposits show no sign whatever of a marine origin. No sea-shells, nor remains of any marine animal, have as yet been found throughout their whole extent, over a region several thousand miles in length and from five to seven hundred miles in width. It is contrary to all our knowledge of geological deposits to suppose that an ocean basin of this size, which must have been submerged during an immensely long period in order to accumulate formations of such a thickness, should not contain numerous remains of the animals formerly inhabiting it.[3] The only fossil remains of any kind truly belonging to it, which I have found in the formation, are leaves taken from the lower clays on the banks of the Solimoens at Tonantins; and these show a vegetation similar in general character to that which prevails there to-day. Evidently, then, this basin was a fresh-water basin; these deposits are fresh-water deposits. But as the valley of the Amazons exists to-day, it is widely open to the ocean on the east, with a gentle slope from the Andes to the Atlantic, determining a powerful seaward current. When these vast accumulations took place, the basin must have been closed; otherwise the loose materials would constantly have been carried down to the ocean.

It is my belief that all these deposits belong to the ice-period in its earlier or later phases, and to this cosmic winter, which, judging from all the phenomena connected with it, may have lasted for thousands of centuries, we must look for the key to the geological history of the Amazonian Valley. I am aware that this suggestion will appear extravagant. But is it, after all, so improbable that, when Central Europe was covered with ice thousands of feet thick; when the glaciers of Great Britain ploughed into the sea, and when those of the Swiss mountains had ten times their present altitude; when every lake in Northern Italy was filled with ice, and these frozen masses extended even into Northern Africa; when a sheet of ice, reaching nearly to the summit of Mount Washington in the White Mountains (that is, having a thickness of nearly six thousand feet), moved over the continent of North America—is it so improbable that, in this epoch of universal cold, the valley of the Amazons also had its glacier poured down into it from the accumulations of snow in the Cordilleras, and swollen laterally by the tributary glaciers descending from the table-lands of Guiana and Brazil? The movement of this immense glacier must have been eastward, determined as well by the vast reservoirs of snow in the Andes as by the direction of the valley itself. It must have ploughed the valley-bottom over and over again, grinding all the materials beneath it into a fine powder or reducing them to small pebbles, and it must have accumulated at its lower end a moraine of proportions as gigantic as its own; thus building a colossal sea-wall across the mouth of the valley. I shall be asked at once whether I have found here also the glacial inscriptions—the furrows, striae, and polished surfaces so characteristic of the ground over which glaciers have travelled. I answer, not a trace of them; for the simple reason that there is not a natural rock-surface to be found throughout the whole Amazonian Valley. The rocks themselves are of so friable a nature, and the decomposition caused by the warm torrential rains and by exposure to the burning sun of the tropics so great and unceasing, that it is hopeless to look for marks which in colder climates and on harder substances are preserved through ages unchanged. With the exception of the rounded surfaces so well known in Switzerland as the *roches moutonnées* heretofore alluded to, which may be seen in many localities, and the boulders of Erere, the direct traces of glaciers as seen in other countries are wanting in Brazil. I am, indeed, quite willing to admit that, from the nature of the circumstances, I have not here the positive evidence which has guided me in my previous glacial investigations. My conviction in this instance is founded, first, on the materials in the Amazonian Valley, which correspond exactly in their character to materials accumulated in glacier bottoms; secondly, on the resemblance of the upper or third Amazonian formation to the Rio drift,[4] of the glacial origin of which there cannot, in my opinion, be any doubt; thirdly, on the fact that this fresh-water basin must have been closed against the sea by some powerful barrier, the removal of which would naturally give an outlet to the waters, and cause the extraordinary denudations, the evidences of which meet us everywhere throughout the valley.

On a smaller scale, phenomena of this kind have long been familiar to us. In the present lakes of Northern Italy, in those of Switzerland, Norway, and Sweden, as well as in those of New England, especially in the State of Maine, the waters are held back in their basins by moraines. In the ice-period these depressions were filled with glaciers, which, in the course of time, accumulated at their lower end a wall of loose materials. These walls still remain, and serve as dams to prevent the escape of the waters. But for their moraines, all these lakes would be open valleys. In the Roads of Glen Roy, in Scotland, we have an instance of a fresh-water lake, which has now wholly disappeared, formed in the same manner, and reduced successively to lower and lower levels by the breaking down or wearing away of the moraines which originally prevented its waters from flowing out. Assuming then that, under the low temperature of the ice-period, the climatic conditions necessary for the formation of land-ice existed in the valley of the Amazons, and that it was actually filled with an immense glacier, it follows that, when these fields of ice yielded to a gradual change of climate, and slowly melted away, the whole basin, then closed against the sea by a huge wall of *debris*, was transformed into a vast fresh-water lake. The first effect of the thawing process must have been to separate the glacier from its foundation, raising it from immediate contact with the valley bottom, and thus giving room for the accumulation of a certain amount of water beneath it; while the valley as a whole would still be occupied by the glacier. In this shallow sheet of water under the ice, and protected by it from any violent disturbance, those finer triturated materials always found at a glacier bottom, and ground sometimes to powder by its action, would be deposited, and gradually transformed from an unstratified paste containing the finest sand and mud, together with coarse pebbles and gravel, into a regularly stratified formation. In this formation the coarse materials would of course fall to the bottom, while the most minute would settle above them. It is at this time and under such circumstances that I believe the first formation of the Amazonian Valley, with the coarse, pebbly sand beneath, and the finely laminated clays above, to have been accumulated.

I shall perhaps be reminded here of my fossil leaves, and asked how any vegetation would be possible under such circumstances. But it must be remembered, that, in considering all these periods, we must allow for immense lapses of time and for very gradual changes; that the close of this first period would be very different from its beginning; and that a rich vegetation springs on the very borders of the snow and ice fields in Switzerland. The fact that these were accumulated in a glacial basin would, indeed, at once account for the traces of vegetable life, and for the absence, or at least the great scarcity, of animal remains in these deposits. For while fruits may ripen and flowers bloom on the very edge of the glaciers, it is also well known that the fresh-water lakes formed by the melting of the ice are singularly deficient in life. There are, indeed, hardly any animals to be found in glacial lakes.

The second formation belongs to a later period, when, the whole body of ice being more or less disintegrated, the basin contained a larger quantity of water. Beside that arising from the melting of the ice, this immense valley bottom must have received, then as now, all which was condensed from the atmosphere above, and poured into it in the form of rain or dew at present. Thus an amount of water equal to that flowing in from all the tributaries of the main stream must have been rushing towards the axis of the valley, seeking its natural level, but spreading over a more extensive surface than now, until, finally gathered up as separate rivers, it flowed in distinct beds. In its general movement toward the central and lower part of the valley, the broad stream would carry along all the materials small enough to be so transported, as well as those so minute as to remain suspended in the waters. It would gradually deposit them in the valley bottom in horizontal beds more or less regular, or here and there, wherever eddies gave rise to more rapid and irregular currents, characterized by torrential stratification. Thus has been consolidated in the course of ages the continuous sand formation spreading over the whole Amazonian basin, and attaining a thickness of eight hundred feet.

While these accumulations were taking place within this basin, it must not be forgotten that the sea was beating against its outer wall—against that gigantic moraine which I suppose to have closed it at its eastern end. It would seem that, either from this cause, or perhaps in consequence of some turbulent action from within, a break was made in this defence, and the waters rushed violently out. It is very possible that the waters, gradually swollen at the close of this period by the further melting of the ice, by the additions poured in from lateral tributaries, by the rains, and also by the filling of the basin with loose materials, would overflow, and thus contribute to destroy the moraine. However this may be, it follows from my premises that, in the end, these waters obtained a sudden release, and poured seaward with a violence which cut and denuded the deposits already formed, wearing them down to a much lower level, and leaving only a few remnants standing out in their original thickness, where the strata were solid enough to resist the action of the currents. Such as the hills of Monte Alegre, of Obydos, Almeyrim, and Cupati, as well as the lower ridges of Santarem. This escape of the waters did not, however, entirely empty the whole basin; for the period of denudation was again followed by one of quiet accumulation, during which was deposited the ochraceous sandy clay resting upon the denudated surfaces of the underlying sandstone. To this period I refer the boulders of Erere, sunk as they are in the clay of this final deposit. I suppose them to have been brought to their present position by floating ice at the close of the glacial period, when nothing remained of the ice-fields except such isolated masses—ice-rafts as it were; or perhaps by icebergs dropped into the basin from glaciers still remaining in the Andes and on the edges of the plateaus of Guiana and Brazil. From the general absence of stratification in this clay formation, it would seem that the comparatively shallow sheet of water in which it was deposited was very tranquil. Indeed, after the waters had sunk much below the level which they held during the deposition of the sandstone, and the currents which gave rise to the denudation of the latter had ceased, the whole sheet of water would naturally become much more placid. But the time arrived when the water broke through its boundaries again, perhaps owing to the further encroachment of the sea and consequent destruction of the moraine.[5] In this second drainage, however, the waters, carrying away a considerable part of the new deposit, furrowing it to its very foundation, and even cutting through it into the underlying sandstone, were, in the end, reduced to something like their present level, and confined within their present beds. This is shown by the fact that in this ochre-colored clay, and penetrating to a greater or less depth the sandstone below, are dug, not only the great longitudinal channel of the Amazons itself, but also the lateral furrows through which its tributaries reach the main stream, and the network of anastomosing branches flowing between them; the whole forming the most extraordinary river system in the world.

My assumption that the sea has produced very extensive changes in the coast of Brazil—changes more than sufficient to account for the disappearance of the glacial wall which I suppose to have closed the Amazonian Valley in the ice period—is by no means hypothetical. This action is still going on to a remarkable degree, and is even now rapidly modifying the outline of the shore. When I first arrived at Para, I was struck with the fact that the Amazons, the largest river in the world, has no delta. All the other rivers which we call great, though some of them are insignificant as compared with the Amazons—the Mississippi, the Nile, the Ganges, and the Danube—deposit extensive deltas, and the smaller rivers also, with few exceptions, are constantly building up the land at their mouths by the materials they bring along with them. Even the little river Kander, emptying into the lake of Thum, is not without its delta. Since my return from the Upper Amazons to Para, I have made an examination of some of the harbor islands, and also parts of the coast, and have satisfied myself that, with the exception of a few small, low islands, never rising above the sea-level, and composed of alluvial deposit, they are portions of the main-land detached from it, partly by the action of the river itself, and partly by the encroachment of the ocean. In fact, the sea is eating away the land much faster than the river can build it up. The great island of Marajo was originally a continuation of the valley of the Amazons, and is identical with it in every detail of its geological structure. My investigation of the island itself, in connection with the coast and the river, leads me to suppose that, having been at one time an integral part of the deposits described above, at a later period it became an island in the bed of the Amazons, which, dividing in two arms, encircled it completely, and then, joining again to form a single stream, flowed onward to the sea-shore, which in those days lay much farther to the eastward than it now does. I suppose the position of the island of Marajo at that time to have corresponded very nearly to the present position of the island of Tupinambaranas, just at the junction of the Madeira with the Amazons. It is a question among geographers whether the Tocantins is a branch of the Amazons, or should be considered as forming an independent river system. It will be seen that, if my view is correct, it must formerly have borne the same relation to the Amazons that the Madeira River now does, joining it just where Marajo divided the main stream, as the Madeira now joins it at the head of the island of Tupinambaranas. If in countless centuries to come the ocean should continue to eat its way into the Valley of the Amazons, once more transforming the lower part of the basin into a gulf, as it was during the cretaceous period, the time might arrive when geographers, finding the Madeira emptying almost immediately into the sea, would ask themselves whether it had ever been indeed a branch of the Amazons, just as they now question whether the Tocantins is a tributary of the main stream or an independent river. But to return to Marajo, and to the facts actually in our possession.

The island is intersected, in its southeastern end, by a considerable river called the Igarape Grande. The cut made through the land by this stream seems intended to serve as a geological section, so perfectly does it display the three characteristic Amazonian formations above described. At its mouth, near the town of Soure, and at Salvaterra, on the opposite bank, may be seen, lowest, the well-stratified sandstone, with the finely laminated clays resting upon it, overtopped by a crust; then the cross-stratified, highly ferruginous sandstone, with quartz pebbles here and there; and, above all, the well-known ochraceous, unstratified sandy clay, spreading over the undulating surface of the denudated sandstone, following all its inequalities, and filling all its depressions and furrows. But while the Igarape Grande has dug its channel down to the sea, cutting these formations, as I ascertained, to a depth of twenty-five fathoms, it has thus opened the way for the encroachments of the tides, and the ocean is now, in its turn, gaining upon the land. Were there no other evidence of the action of the tides in this locality, the steep cut of the Igarape Grande, contrasting with the gentle slope of the banks near its mouth, wherever they have been modified by the invasion of the sea, would enable us to distinguish the work of the river from that of the ocean, and to prove that the denudation now going on is due in part to both. But besides this, I was so fortunate as to discover, on my recent excursion, unmistakable and perfectly convincing evidence of the onward movement of the sea. At the mouth of the Igarape Grande, both at Soure and at Salvaterra, on the southern side of the Igarape, is a submerged forest. Evidently this forest grew in one of those marshy lands constantly inundated, for between the stumps is accumulated the loose, felt-like peat characteristic of such grounds, and containing about as much mud as vegetable matter. Such a marshy forest, with the stumps of the trees still standing erect in the peat, has been laid bare on both sides of the Igarape Grande by the encroachments of the ocean. That this is the work of the sea is undeniable, for all the little depressions and indentations of the peat are filled with sea-sand, and a ridge of tidal sand divides it from the forest still standing behind. Nor is this all. At Vigia, immediately opposite to Soure, on the continental side of the Para River, just where it meets the sea, we have the counterpart of this submerged forest. Another peat-bog, with the stumps of innumerable trees standing in it, and encroached upon in the same way by tidal sand, is exposed here also. No doubt these forests were once all continuous, and stretched across the whole basin of what is now called the Para River.

Since I have been pursuing this inquiry, I have gathered much information to the same effect from persons living on the coast. It is well remembered, that, twenty years ago, there existed an island, more than a mile in width, to the northeast of the entrance of the Bay of Vigia, which has now entirely disappeared. Farther eastward, the Bay of Braganza has doubled its width in the last twenty years, and on the shore, within the bay, the sea has gained upon the land for a distance of two hundred yards during a period of only ten years. The latter fact is ascertained by the position of some houses, which were two hundred yards farther from the sea ten years ago than they now are. From these and the like reports, from my own observations on this part of the Brazilian coast, from some investigations made by Major Coutinho at the mouth of the Amazons on its northern continental shore near Jacapa, and from the reports of Mr. St. John respecting the formations in the valley of the Paranahyba, it is my belief that the changes I have been describing are but a small part of the destruction wrought by the sea on the northeastern shore of this continent. I think it will be found, when the coast has been fully surveyed, that a strip of land not less than a hundred leagues in width, stretching from Cape St. Roque to the northern extremity of South America, has been eaten away by the ocean. If this be so, the Paranahyba and the rivers to the northwest of it, in the province of Maranham, were formerly tributaries of the Amazons; and all that we know thus far of their geological character goes to prove that this was actually the case. Such an extensive oceanic denudation must have carried away not only the gigantic glacial moraine here assumed to have closed the mouth of the Amazonian basin, but the very ground on which it formerly stood. Although the terminal moraine has disappeared, there is, however, no reason why parts of the lateral moraines should not remain. And I expect in my approaching visit to Ceara to find traces of the southern lateral moraine in that neighborhood.

During the last four or five years I have been engaged in a series of investigations, in the United States, upon the subject of the denudations connected with the close of the glacial period there, and the encroachments of the ocean upon the drift deposits along the Atlantic coast. Had these investigations been published in detail, with the necessary maps, it would have been far easier for me to explain the facts I have lately observed in the Amazonian Valley, to connect them with facts of a like character on the continent of North America, and to show how remarkably they correspond with facts accomplished during the same period in other parts of the world. While the glacial epoch itself has been very extensively studied in the last half-century, little attention has been paid to the results connected with the breaking up of the geological winter and the final disappearance of the ice. I believe that the true explanation of the presence of a large part of the superficial deposits lately ascribed to the agency of the sea, during temporary subsidences of the land, will be found in the melting of the ice-fields. To this cause I would refer all those deposits which I have designated as remodelled drift. When the sheet of ice, extending from the Arctic regions over a great part of North America and coming down to the sea, slowly melted away, the waters were not distributed over the face of the country as they now are. They rested upon the bottom deposits of the ice-fields, upon the glacial paste, consisting of clay, sand, pebbles, boulders, etc., underlying the ice. This bottom deposit did not, of course, present an even surface, but must have had extensive undulations and depressions. After the waters had been drained off from the more elevated ridges, these depressions would still remain full. In the lakes and pools thus formed, stratified deposits would be accumulated, consisting of the most minutely comminuted clay, deposited in thin laminated layers, or sometimes in considerable masses, without any sign of stratification; such differences in the formation being determined by the state of the water, whether perfectly stagnant or more or less agitated. Of such pool deposits overlying the drift there are many instances in the Northern United States. By the overflowing of some of these lakes, and by the emptying of the higher ones into those on a lower level, channels would gradually be formed between the depressions. So began to be marked out our independent river-systems—the waters always seeking their natural level, gradually widening and deepening the channels in which they flowed, as they worked their way down to the sea. When they reached the shore, there followed that antagonism between the rush of the rivers and the action of the tides—between continental outflows and oceanic encroachments—which still goes on, and has led to the formation of our Eastern rivers, with their wide, open estuaries, such as the James, the Potomac, and the Delaware. All these estuaries are embanked by drift, as are also, in their lower course, the rivers connected with them. Where the country was low and flat, and the drift extended far into the ocean, the encroachment of the sea gave rise, not only to our large estuaries, but also to the sounds and deep bays forming the most prominent indentations of the continental coast, such as the Bay of Fundy, Massachusetts Bay, Long Island Sound, and others. The unmistakable traces of glacial action upon all the islands along the coast of New England, sometimes lying at a very considerable distance from the main-land, give an approximate, though a minimum, measure of the former extent of the glacial drift seaward, and the subsequent advance of the ocean upon the land. Like those of the harbor of Para, all these islands have the same geological structure as the continent, and were evidently continuous with it at some former period. All the rocky islands along the coast of Maine and Massachusetts exhibit the glacial traces wherever their surfaces are exposed by the washing away of the drift;

and where the drift remains, its character shows that it was once continuous from one island to another, and from all the islands to the main-land.

It is difficult to determine with precision the ancient limit of the glacial drift, but I think it can be shown that it connected the shoals of Newfoundland with the continent; that Nantucket, Martha's Vineyard, and Long Island made part of the main-land; that, in like manner Nova Scotia, including Sable Island, was united to the southern shore of New Brunswick and Maine, and that the same sheet of drift extended thence to Cape Cod, and stretched southward as far as Cape Hatteras;—in short, that the line of shallow soundings along the whole coast of the United States marks the former extent of glacial drift. The ocean has gradually eaten its way into this deposit, and given its present outlines to the continent. These denudations of the sea no doubt began as soon as the breaking up of the ice exposed the drift to its invasion; in other words, at a time when colossal glaciers still poured forth their load of ice into the Atlantic, and fleets of icebergs, far larger and more numerous than those now floated off from the Arctic seas, were launched from the northeastern shore of the United States. Many such masses must have stranded along the shore, and have left various signs of their presence. In fact, the glacial phenomena of the United States and elsewhere are due to two distinct periods: the first of these was the glacial epoch proper, when the ice was a solid sheet; while to the second belongs the breaking up of this epoch, with the gradual disintegration and dispersion of the ice. We talk of the theory of glaciers and the theory of icebergs in reference to these phenomena, as if they were exclusively due to one or the other, and whoever accepted the former must reject the latter, and *vice versa*. When geologists have combined these now discordant elements, and consider these two periods as consecutive—part of the phenomena being due to the glaciers, part to the icebergs and to freshets consequent on their breaking up—they will find that they have covered the whole ground, and that the two theories are perfectly consistent with each other. I think the present disputes upon this subject will end somewhat like those which divided the Neptunic and Plutonic schools of geologists in the early part of this century; the former of whom would have it that all the rocks were due to the action of water, the latter that they were wholly due to the action of fire. The problem was solved, and harmony restored, when it was found that both elements have been equally at work in forming the solid crust of the globe. To the stranded icebergs alluded to above, I have no doubt, is to be referred the origin of the many lakes without outlets existing all over the sandy tract along our coast, of which Cape Cod forms a part. Not only the formation of these lakes, but also that of our salt marshes and cranberry-fields, I believe to be connected with the waning of the ice period.

I hope at some future time to publish in detail, with the appropriate maps and illustrations, my observations upon the changes of our coast, and other phenomena connected with the close of the glacial epoch in the United States. To give results without an account of the investigations which have led to them, inverts the true method of science; and I should not have introduced the subject here except to show that the fresh-water denudations and the oceanic encroachments which have formed the Amazonian Valley, with its river system, are not isolated facts, but that the process has been the same in both continents. The extraordinary continuity and uniformity of the Amazonian deposits are due to the immense size of the basin enclosed, and the identity of the materials contained in it.

A glance at any geological map of the world will show the reader that the Valley of the Amazons, so far as an attempt is made to explain its structure, is represented as containing isolated tracts of Devonian, Triassic, Jurassic, cretaceous, tertiary, and alluvial deposits. This is wholly inaccurate, as is shown by the above sketch, and whatever may be thought of my interpretation of the actual phenomena, I trust that, in presenting for the first time the formations of the Amazonian basin in their natural connection and sequence, as consisting of three uniform sets of comparatively recent deposits, extending throughout the whole valley, the investigations here recorded have contributed something to the results of modern geology.

CHAPTER IV.

Voyage up the Coast to Para.

July 25th.—On board the "Cruzeiro do Sul." We sailed to-day at 11 o'clock, bidding good by with regret, though not without hope of return, to the beautiful bay and mountains on which we have been looking for three months. Our party consists of Major Coutinho, Mr. Burkhardt, Monsieur Bourget, who accompanies Mr. Agassiz to the Amazons as collector and preparator, our two young friends Mr. Hunnewell and Mr. James, and ourselves. At Bahia we shall be joined by Mr. Dexter and Mr. Thayer, two of our party who have preceded us up the coast, and have been collecting in the neighborhood of Bahia for two or three weeks. The aspect of the steamer is not very inviting, for it has been used of late for the transportation of troops to the south, in consequence of which it is very dirty; it is also overcrowded on account of the number of persons bound northward, who have been detained in Rio by the interruption of the regular trips on this line. We are promised better accommodations after a few days, however, as many of the passengers will drop off at Bahia and Pernambuco.

July 28th.—Bahia. Half the enjoyment of life borrows intensity from contrast, and to this principle we certainly owe a part of our pleasure to-day. After three half seasick days on a dirty, crowded steamer, the change is delightful to a breezy country house, where we are received with that most gracious hospitality which relieves both host and guests of the sense of entertaining or being entertained. Here I have been sitting under the deep shade of a huge mango-tree, with a number of the "Revue des Deux Mondes" on my knee, either reading or listening lazily to the rustle of the leaves or the cooing of the pigeons as they patter up and down on the tiled floor of the porch near by, or watching the negroes as they come and go with trays of vegetables or baskets of fruit and flowers on their heads, for the service of the house. In the mean time, Mr. Agassiz is engaged in examining the collections made by Mr. Dexter and Mr. Thayer during their visit here. They have been aided most cordially by our friend Mr. Antonio de Lacerda, at whose hospitable house we are staying, and where we found our travelling companions quite domesticated. He received them on their arrival, and has given them every facility during their stay here for the objects they had in view, his own love of natural history, to which he devotes every spare hour from his active business life, rendering him an efficient ally. He has a large and very valuable collection of insects, admirably arranged and in excellent preservation. They are also greatly indebted to Mr. Nicolai, the resident English clergyman here, who has accompanied them on some of their excursions, and put them in the way of seeing whatever was most interesting in the neighborhood.

On arriving in South America one should land first in Bahia, for in its aspect it is the most national and characteristic of the cities. As we passed directly through the town this morning, we can give but little account of it, and yet we saw enough to confirm all that has been said of its quaint and picturesque character. On first disembarking, you find yourself at the foot of an almost perpendicular hill, and negro-bearers appear at your side to carry you up the steep ascent, almost impassable for carriages, in a "cadeira," or curtained chair. This is in itself an odd experience for one to whom it is new, and the rest of the city, with its precipitous streets, its queer houses, its old churches, is as quaint and antique as these original carriages.

JULY 29th.—To-day we have the "revers de la medaille"; we have returned to our prison, and a violent rain drives us all to take refuge in the hot, close dining-room, our only resort when the weather is bad.

JULY 30th.—Off Maceio. Last evening, when the rain was over and the moonlight tempted every one on deck, we had a long conversation with our pleasant travelling companion, Mr. Sinimbu, senator from the province of Alagôas, on the aspect of slavery in Brazil. It seems to me that we may have something to learn here in our own perplexities respecting the position of the black race among us, for the Brazilians are trying gradually and by installments some of the experiments which are forced upon us without previous preparation. The absence of all restraint upon the free blacks, the fact that they are eligible to office, and that all professional careers are open to them, without prejudice on the ground of color, enables one to form some opinion as to their ability and capacity for development. Mr. Sinimbu tells us that here the result is on the whole in their favor; he says that the free blacks compare well in intelligence and activity with the Brazilians and Portuguese. But it must be remembered, in making the comparison with reference to our own country, that here they are brought into contact with a less energetic and powerful race than the Anglo-Saxon. Mr. Sinimbu believes that emancipation is to be accomplished in Brazil by a gradual process which has already begun. A large number of slaves are freed every year by the wills of their masters; a still larger number buy their own freedom annually; and as there is no longer any importation of blacks, the inevitable result of this must be the natural death of slavery. Unhappily, the process is a slow one, and in the mean while slavery is doing its evil work, debasing and enfeebling alike whites and blacks. The Brazilians themselves do not deny this, and one constantly hears them lament the necessity of sending their children away to be educated, on account of the injurious association with the house-servants. In fact, although politically slavery has a more hopeful aspect here than elsewhere, the institution from a moral point of view has some of its most revolting characters in this country, and looks, if possible, more odious than it did in the States. The other day, in the neighborhood of Rio, I had an opportunity of seeing a marriage between two negroes, whose owner made the religious, or, as it appeared to me on this occasion, irreligious ceremony, obligatory. The bride, who was as black as jet, was dressed in white muslin, with a veil of coarse white lace, such as the negro women make themselves, and the husband was in a white linen suit. She looked, and I think she really felt, diffident, for there were a good many strangers present, and her position was embarrassing. The Portuguese priest, a bold, insolent-looking man, called them up and rattled over the marriage service with most irreverent speed, stopping now and then to scold them both, but especially the woman, because she did not speak loud enough and did not take the whole thing in the same coarse, rough way that he did. When he ordered them to come up and kneel at the altar, his tone was more suggestive of cursing than praying, and having uttered his blessing he hurled an amen at them, slammed the prayer-book down on the altar, whiffed out the candles, and turned the bride and bridegroom out of the chapel with as little ceremony as one would have kicked out a dog. As the bride came out, half crying, half smiling, her mother met her and showered her with rose-leaves, and so this act of consecration in which the mother's benediction seemed the only grace, was over. I thought what a strange confusion there must be in these poor creature's minds, if they thought about it at all. They are told that the relation between man and wife is a sin, unless confirmed by the sacred rite of marriage; they come to hear a bad man gabble over them words which they cannot understand, mingled with taunts and abuse which they understand only too well, and side by side with their own children grow up the little fair-skinned slaves to tell them practically that the white man does not keep himself the law he imposes on them. What a monstrous lie the whole system must seem to them if they are ever led to think about it at all. I am far from supposing that the instance I have given should be taken as representing the state of religious instruction on plantations generally. No doubt there are good priests who improve and instruct their black parishioners; but it does not follow because religious services are provided on a plantation, the ceremony of marriage observed, &c., that there is anything which deserves the name of religious instruction. It would be unjust not to add the better side of the question in this particular instance. The man was free, and I was told that the woman received her liberty and a piece of land from her master as her marriage dower.

We arrived at Maceio this morning, and went on shore with Mr. Sinimbu, who leaves us here, and with whose family we passed a delightful day, welcomed with that hearty cordiality so characteristic of Brazilians in their own homes. Although our stay was so short, a considerable addition was made here to the collections. On arriving at any port the party disperses at once, the young men going in different directions to collect, Mr. Bourget hurrying to the fish-market to see what may be found there of interest, and Mr. Agassiz and Mr. Coutinho generally making a geological excursion. In this way, though the steamer remains but a few hours at each station, the time is not lost.

JULY 31st.—Pernambuco. Arrived to-day off Pernambuco, and were too happy, after a stormy night, to find ourselves behind the famous reef which makes such a quiet harbor at this port. Our countryman, Mr. Hitch, met us on landing, and drove us at once out to his "chacara," (country place,) where it was delightful to be welcomed, like old friends, to an American home.[6] Pernambuco is by no means so picturesque as Bahia or Rio de Janeiro. It has a more modern air than either of these, but looks also more cleanly and more prosperous. Many of the streets are wide, and the river running through the business part of the city, crossed by broad, handsome bridges, is itself suggestive of freshness. The country is more open and flat than farther south. In our afternoon drive some of the views across wide, level meadows, if we could have put elms here and there in the place of palms, would have reminded us of scenery at home.

AUGUST 2d.—Yesterday we left Pernambuco, and this morning found ourselves at the mouth of the Parahyba do Norte, a broad, beautiful river, up which we steamed to within a few miles of the little town bearing the same name. Here we took a boat and rowed to the city, where we spent some hours in rambling about, collecting specimens, examining drift formations, &c. In the course of our excursion we fell in with some friends of Major Coutinho's, who took us home with them to an excellent breakfast of fresh fish, with bread, coffee, and wine. The bread is to be noticed here, for it is said to be the best in Brazil. The flour is the same as elsewhere, and the people generally attribute the superiority of their bread to some quality of the water. Whatever be the cause, there is no bread in all Brazil so sweet, so light, and so white as that of Parahyba do Norte.

AUGUST 5th.—We arrived yesterday at Ceara, where we were warmly welcomed and most hospitably entertained at the house of Dr. Mendes, an old acquaintance of Major Coutinho. It was blowing hard and raining when two of our negro rowers jumped into the water, and, standing at the side of the boat behind me, motioned me to come, crossing their arms basket-fashion, as we do sometimes to carry children. They looked as if it were the ordinary mode of conveyance, so I seated myself, and with one arm around the neck of each of my black bearers, they laughing as heartily as I did, I was landed triumphantly on the sands. After the first greetings at the house of Dr. Mendes were over, we were offered the luxury of a bath before breakfast. The bath is a very important feature in a Brazilian household. This one was of the size of a small room, the water (about two feet deep and of a delicious, soft, velvety character) constantly flowing through over the smooth sand floor. They are often larger than this, from four to five feet deep, and sometimes lined with blue and white tiles, which make a very clean and pretty floor. It is a great luxury in this warm climate, and many persons bathe several times a day. The bath-house is usually in the garden, at a convenient distance from the house but not immediately adjoining it. The bath was followed by an excellent breakfast, after which we drove through the city. Ceara is a wonderfully progressive town from Brazil. Five years ago it had not a paved street; now all the streets are well paved, with good sidewalks, and the city is very carefully laid out, with a view to its future growth.[7] To-day we are again coasting along within sight of land, with a quiet sea and a delicious breeze. The ocean is covered with white caps, and of a very peculiar greenish aquamarine tint, the same which I observed as soon as we reached these latitudes in coming out. This singular color is said to be owing to the nature of the sea bottom and the shallowness of the water, combined, farther north, with the admixture of fresh water along the coast.

AUGUST 6th.—Arrived early this morning before Maranham, and went on shore to breakfast at the hotel; for, wonderful to relate, Maranham possesses a hotel, a great rarity in many Brazilian towns. We passed the greater part of the day in driving about the city with Dr. Braga, who kindly undertook to show us everything of interest.[8] The town and harbor are very pretty, the city itself standing on an island, formed by two bays running up on either side and enclosing it. The surrounding country is flat and very thickly wooded, though the woods are rather low. Here, at the house of Dr. Braga's brother-in-law, we saw, for the first time,

the slender, graceful Assai palm, from which the drink is made so
much appreciated in Para and on the Lower Amazons. It is curious to see the negroes go up the tree to gather the fruit. The trunk
is perfectly smooth, the fruit growing in a heavy cluster of berries,
just below the crown of leaves on its summit. The negro fastens
a cord or a strip of palm-leaf around his insteps, thus binding
his feet together that they may not slide apart on the smooth
stem, and by means of this kind of stirrup he contrives to cling
to the slippery trunk and scramble up.

We were much interested in seeing here an admirably well
conducted institution for the education of poor orphans. Its chief
aim is to educate them, not as scholars, though they receive elementary instruction in reading, writing, and ciphering, but to
teach them a variety of occupations by which they can earn an
honest livelihood. They are trained in several trades, are taught
to play on a number of instruments, and there is also a school of
design connected with the establishment. A faultless order and
scrupulous neatness prevailed through the whole building, which
was not the result of an exceptional preparation, since our visit
was wholly unexpected. This surprised us the more, because,
notwithstanding their fondness for bathing, order and neatness
in their houses are not a virtue among the Brazilians. This may
be owing to slave labor—rarely anything better than eye-service.
The large dormitories looked fresh and airy, with the hammocks
rolled up and laid on a shelf, each one above the peg to which it
belonged; the shoes were hung on nails along the walls, and the
little trunks, holding the clothing of each scholar, were neatly
arranged beneath them. On the upper story was the hospital, a
large, well-ventilated room, with numerous windows commanding beautiful views, and a cool breeze blowing through it. Here
were cots instead of hammocks, but I thought the sick boys might
prefer the swinging, cradle-like beds to which they were accustomed, and which they evidently find very comfortable. When
Mr. Agassiz remarked, as we passed through the dormitory, that
sleeping in a hammock was an experience he had yet to make,
one of the boys took his down from the shelf, and hanging it up,
laughingly threw himself into it, with a lazy ease which looked
quite enviable. The kitchen and grocery rooms were as neat as

the rest of the house, and the simplicity of the whole establishment, while it admitted everything necessary for comfort and health, was well adapted for its objects. A pretty little chapel adjoined the house, and the house itself was built around an open square planted with trees—a pleasant playground for the boys, who have their music there in the evening. On our return to town we heard that, owing to the breakage of some part of the machinery, the steamer would be detained in this port for a couple of days. We have, however, returned to our quarters on board, preferring to spend the night on the water rather than in the hot, close town.

AUGUST 7th.—To-day we have all been interested in watching the beautiful Medusae swept along by the tide, so close to the side of the steamer that they could easily be reached from the stairway. We have now quite a number disposed about the deck in buckets and basins, and Mr. Burkhardt is making colored sketches of them. They are very beautiful, and quite new to Mr. Agassiz. In some the disk has a brown tracery like seaweed over it, while its edge is deeply lobed, every lobe being tinged with an intensely brilliant dark blue; the lobes are divided into eight sets of four each, making thirty-two in all, and an eye is placed on the margin between each set; the tubes running to the eyes are much larger than those in the intervals between, and the network of vessels on the margin is wonderfully fine and delicate; the curtains hanging from the mouth are white and closely fringed with full flounces, somewhat like our Aurelia. The movement is quick, the margin of the disk beating with short, rapid pants. Another is altogether brown and white, the seaweed-like pattern being carried down to the edge of the lobes, and the lobes themselves being more delicate than those of the blue-edged one, the disk thinning out greatly towards the periphery. The brown marks are, however, darker, more distinct, and cover a larger space in some specimens than in others. This is also true of those with the blue margin, the brown pattern covering the whole disk in some, confined to a simple zone around the disk in others, and even entirely absent occasionally. Mr. Agassiz inclines to think, from the similarity of their other features, however, that notwithstanding their difference of color, they all belong to the same species, the

variety in coloration being probably connected with difference
of sex. He has, at any rate, ascertained that all the wholly brown
specimens caught to-day are males.

We were rejoiced this morning by the sight of our own flag
coming into harbor. We presently found that the ship was the
gunboat Nipsic. She had sailed from Boston on the 4th of July,
and brought papers of a later date than any we have seen. The
officers were kind enough to send us a large bundle of papers,
which we have been eagerly devouring.

AUGUST 8th.—Another quite new and beautiful Medusa to-
day. As we were waiting for breakfast this morning a number
floated past, so dark in color that in the water they appeared almost black. Two of our party took a boat and went in search
of them, but the tide was so swift that they swept past like light-
ning, and one had hardly time to point them out before they
were gone again. However, after many efforts, we succeeded in
getting one, whose portrait Mr. Burkhardt is now taking. The
disk is of a chocolate brown, shading into a darker, more velvety
hue toward the edge, which is slightly scalloped, but not cut up
into deep lobes like those of yesterday. The eyes, eight in number,
are distinctly visible as lighter-colored specks on the margin. The
appendages hanging from the mouth are more solid and not so
thickly fringed as in those of yesterday. It moves rather slowly in
its glass prison, the broad margin shading from lighter brown to
a soft chocolate color almost verging on black, as it flaps up and
down somewhat languidly, but still with a regular, steady pulsa-
tion.[9]

AUGUST 9th.—We passed yesterday afternoon with the Braga
family in town. The weather was charming, a cool breeze blowing through the veranda where we dined. There were a number of guests to meet us, and we had again cause to acknowledge
how completely the stranger is made to feel himself at
home among these hospitable people. We sailed this morning,
Mr. Agassiz taking with him a valuable collection, though our
time was so short. The fact is, that, not only here, but at every
town where we have stopped in coming up the coast, the ready,
cordial desire of the people to help in the work has enabled him
to get together collections which it would otherwise have been

impossible to make in so short a time. If he is unexpectedly successful in this expedition, it is as much owing to the active sympathy of the Brazilians themselves, and to their interest in the object he has so much at heart, as to the efforts of himself and his companions.

AUGUST 11th.—Para. Early yesterday morning, a few yellowish patches staining the ocean here and there gave us our first glimpse of the water of the Amazons. Presently the patches became broad streaks, the fresh waters encroaching gradually upon the sea, until, at about ten o'clock, we fairly entered the mouth of the river, though, as the shores are some hundred and fifty miles apart, we might have believed ourselves on the broad ocean. As we neared the city, the numerous islands closing up about Para and sheltering its harbor limited the view and broke the enormous expanse of the fresh-water basin. We anchored off the city at about three o'clock, but a heavy thunder-shower, with violent rain, prevented us from going on shore till the next morning. None of the party landed except Major Coutinho. He went to announce our arrival to his friend, Mr. Pimenta Bueno, who has kindly invited us to make his house our home while we stay in Para. The next morning was beautiful after the rain, and at seven o'clock two boats were sent to take us and our effects on shore. On landing we went at once to Mr. Pimenta's large business establishment near the wharves. Here he has provided several excellent working-rooms to serve as laboratories and storage-places for the specimens, and besides these a number of airy, cool chambers on the floor above, for the accommodation of our companions, who have already slung their hammocks, arranged their effects, and are keeping a kind of bachelor's hall. Having disposed of the scientific apparatus, we drove out to Mr. Pimenta's "chacara," some two miles out of town, on the Rua de Nazareth, where we were received with the utmost kindness. Mr. Agassiz and Major Coutinho soon returned to town, where no time is to be lost in beginning work at the laboratory. I remained at home and passed a pleasant morning with the ladies of the family, who made me acquainted with the peculiar beverage so famous in these regions, prepared from the berries of the Assai palm. They are about the size of cranberries, and of a dark-brown

color. Being boiled and crushed they yield a quantity of juice,
which when strained has about the consistency of chocolate,
and is of a dark purplish tint like blackberry juice. It has a sweet-
ish taste, and is very nice eaten with sugar and the crisp "farinha
d'agua," a kind of coarse flour made from the mandioca root.
People of all classes throughout the province of Para are exceedingly fond of this beverage, and in the city they have a proverb
which runs thus:—

> Who visits Para is glad to stay,
> Who drinks Assai goes never away.

AUGUST 12th.—This morning we rose early and walked into
town. Great pains have been taken with the environs of Para,
and the Rua de Nazareth is one of the broad streets leading into
the country, and planted with large trees (chiefly mangueiras)
for two or three miles out of town. On our way we saw a lofty
palm-tree completely overpowered and stifled in the embrace of
an enormous parasite. So luxuriant is the growth of the latter that
you do not perceive, till it is pointed out to you, that its spreading branches and thick foliage completely hide the tree from
which it derives its life; only from the extreme summit a few fan-
like palm-leaves shoot upwards as if trying to escape into the air
and light. The palm cannot long survive, however, and with its
death it seals the doom of its murderer also. There is another evidence, and a more pleasing one, of the luxuriance of nature on
this same road. The skeleton of a house stands by the wayside;
whether a ruin or unfinished, I am unable to say, but at all events
only the walls are standing, with the openings for doors and windows. Nature has completed this imperfect dwelling;—she has
covered it over with a green roof, she has planted the empty en-
closure with a garden of her own choosing, she has trained vines
around the open doors and windows; and the deserted house, if
it has no other inmates, is at least a home for the birds. It makes
a very pretty picture. I never pass it without wishing for a sketch
of it. On our arrival in town we went at once to the market. It is
very near the water, and we were much amused in watching the
Indian canoes at the landing. The "montaria," as the Indian calls

his canoe, is a long, narrow boat, covered at one end with a thatched roof, under which is the living-room of the family. Here the Indian has his home; wife and children, hammock, cooking utensils—all his household goods, in fact. In some of the boats the women were preparing breakfast, cooking the coffee or the tapioca over a pan of coals. In others they were selling the coarse pottery, which they make into all kinds of utensils, sometimes of quite graceful, pretty forms. We afterwards went through the market. It is quite large and neatly kept; but the Brazilian markets are only good as compared with each other. The meats are generally poor; there is little game to be seen; they have no variety of vegetables, which might be so easily cultivated here, and even the display of fruit in the market is by no means what one would expect it to be. To-night Mr. Agassiz goes off with a party of gentlemen on an excursion to some of the islands in the harbor. This first expedition in the neighborhood of Para, from which the Professor promises himself much pleasure, is planned by Dr. Couto de Magalhaês, President of the Province.[10]

AUGUST 14th.—We are very agreeably surprised in the climate here. I had expected from the moment of our arrival in the region of the Amazons to be gasping in a fierce, unintermitting, intolerable heat. On the contrary, the mornings are fresh; a walk or ride between six and eight o'clock is always delightful; and though during the middle of the day the heat is certainly very great, it cools off again towards four o'clock; the evenings are delightful, and the nights always comfortable. Even in the hottest part of the day the heat is not dead; there is always a breeze stirring. Mr. Agassiz returned this afternoon from his excursion in the harbor, more deeply impressed than ever with the grandeur of this entrance to the Amazons and the beauty of its many islands, "An archipelago of islands," as he says, "in an ocean of fresh water." He describes the mode of fishing of the Indians as curious. They row very softly up the creek, having first fastened the seine across from shore to shore at a lower point, and when they have gained a certain distance above it, they spring into the water with a great plash and rush down the creek in a line, driving the fish before them into the net. One draught alone filled the boat half full of fish. Mr. Agassiz was especially interested in seeing alive for the first time the curious fish called "Tral-hote" by the Indians, and known to naturalists as the Anableps tetrophthalmus. This name, signifying "four-eyed," is derived from the singular structure of the eye. A membranous fold enclosing the bulb of the eye stretches across the pupil, dividing the visual apparatus into an upper and lower half. No doubt this formation is intended to suit the peculiar habits of the Anableps. These fishes gather in shoals on the surface of the water, their heads resting partly above, partly below the surface, and they move by a leaping motion somewhat like that of frogs on land. Thus, half in air, half in water, they require eyes adapted for seeing in both elements, and the arrangement described above just meets this want.

AUGUST 19th.—To-night at ten o'clock we go on board the steamer, and before dawn shall be on our way up the river. This has been a delicious week of rest and refreshment to me. The quiet country life, with morning walks in the fresh, fragrant lanes and roads immediately about us, has been very soothing after four months of travel or of noisy hotel life. The other day as we were going into town we found in the wet grass by the roadside one of the most beautiful mushrooms I have ever seen. The stem was pure white, three or four inches in height, and about half an inch in diameter, surmounted by a club-shaped head, brown in color, with a blunt point, and from the base of this head was suspended an open white net of exquisitely delicate texture, falling to within about an inch of the ground; a fairy web that looked fit for Queen Mab herself.[11] The week, so peaceful for me, has been one, if not of rest, at least of intense interest for Mr. Agassiz. The very day of his arrival, by the kindness of our host, his working-rooms were so arranged as to make an admirable laboratory, and, from the hour he entered them, specimens have poured in upon him from all quarters. His own party make but a small part of the scientific corps who have worked for and with him here. In Para alone he has already more than fifty new species of fresh-water fishes; enough to reveal unexpected and novel relations in the finny world, and to give the basis of an improved classification. He is far from attributing this great success wholly to his own efforts. Ready as he is to work, he could not accomplish half that he does, except for the active good-will of those about him. Among the most valuable of these contributions is a collection made by Mr. Pimenta Bueno, of the so-called fishes of the forest. When the waters overflow after the rainy season and fill the forest for a considerable distance on either side, these fish hover over the depressions and hollows, and as the waters subside are left in the pools and channels. They do not occur in the open river, but are always found in these forest retreats, and go by the name of the "Peixe do Mato."

Mr. Agassiz has not only to acknowledge the untiring kindness of individuals here, but also the cordial expression of sympathy from public bodies in the objects of the expedition. A committee from the municipality of the city has waited upon him to express the general satisfaction in the undertaking, and he has received a public demonstration of the same kind from the college. The bishop of the province and his coadjutor have also been most cordial in offers of assistance. Nor does the interest thus expressed evaporate in empty words. Mr. Pimenta Bueno is director of the Brazilian line of steamers from Para to Tabatinga.[12] The trip to Manaos, at the mouth of the Rio Negro, is generally made in five days, allowing only for stoppages of an hour or two at different stations, to take or leave passengers and to deposit or receive merchandise. In order that we may be perfectly independent, however, and stop wherever it seems desirable to make collections, the company places at our disposition a steamer for one month between Para and Manaos. There are to be no passengers but ourselves, and the steamer is provided with everything necessary for the whole company during that period—food, service, &c. I think it may fairly be said that in no part of the world could a private scientific undertaking be greeted with more cordiality or receive a more liberal hospitality than has been accorded to the present expedition. I dwell upon these things and recur to them often, not in any spirit of egotism, but because it is due to the character of the people from whom they come to make the fullest acknowledgement of their generosity.

While Mr. Agassiz has been busy with the zoological collections, Major Coutinho has been no less so in making geological, meteorological, and hydrographic investigations. His regular co-operation is invaluable, and Mr. Agassiz blesses the day when

their chance meeting at the Palace suggested the idea of his joining the expedition. Not only his scientific attainments, but his
knowledge of the Indian language (*lingua geral*), and his familiarity with the people, make him a most important coadjutor.
With his aid Mr. Agassiz has already opened a sort of scientific
log-book, in which, by the side of the scientific name of every
specimen entered by the Professor, Major Coutinho records its
popular local name, obtained from the Indians, with all they can
tell of its haunts and habits.

I have said nothing of Mr. Agassiz's observations on the character of the soil since we left Rio, thinking it best to give them as
a whole. Along the entire length of the coast he has followed the
drift, examining it carefully at every station. At Bahia it contained
fewer large boulders than in Rio, but was full of small pebbles,
and rested upon undecomposed stratified rock. At Maceio, the
capital of the province of Alagôas, it was the same, but resting
upon decomposed rock, as at Tijuca. Below this was a bed of
stratified clay, containing small pebbles. In Pernambuco, on our
drive to the great aqueduct, we followed it for the whole way;
the same red clayey homogeneous paste, resting there on decomposed rock. The line of contact at Monteiro, the aqueduct station, was very clearly marked, however, by an intervening bed
of pebbles. At Parahyba do Norte the same sheet of drift, but
containing more and larger pebbles, rests above a decomposed
sandstone somewhat resembling the decomposed rock of Pernambuco. In the undecomposed rock below, Mr. Agassiz found
some fossil shells. In the neighborhood of Cape St. Roque we
came upon sand-dunes resembling those of Cape Cod, and wherever we sailed near enough to the shore to see the banks distinctly,
as was frequently the case, the bed of drift below the shifting
superficial sands above was distinctly noticeable. The difference
in color between the white sand and the reddish soil beneath
made it easy to perceive their relations. At Ceara, where we
landed, Mr. Agassiz had an opportunity of satisfying himself of
this by closer examination. At Maranham the drift is everywhere
conspicuous, and at Para equally so. This sheet of drift which he
has thus followed from Rio de Janeiro to the mouth of the Amazons is everywhere of the same geological constitution. It is al-

ways a homogeneous clayey paste of a reddish color, containing quartz pebbles; and, whatever be the character of the rock in place, whether granite, sandstone, gneiss, or lime, the character of the drift never changes or partakes of that of the rocks with which it is in contact. This certainly proves that, whatever be its origin, it cannot be referred to the localities where it is now found, but must have been brought from a distance. Whoever shall track it back to the place where this peculiar red soil with its constituent elements forms the primitive rock, will have solved the problem. I introduce here a letter written originally in French by Mr. Agassiz, a few days later, to the Emperor, which will better give his views on the subject.

ON BOARD THE ICAMIABA, ON THE AMAZONS,
August 20, 1865

SIRE:—Allow me to give your Majesty a rapid sketch of the most interesting facts observed by me since leaving Rio. The first thing which struck me on arriving at Bahia was the presence of the erratic soil, corresponding to that of Tijuca and the southern part of Minas-Geraes, which I have visited. Here, as there, this soil, identical in its constitution, rests upon rocks in place, of the most diversified character. I have found it also at Maceio, at Pernambuco, at Parahyba do Norte, at Ceara, at Maranham, and at Para. This is a fact, then, established on the largest scale. It shows that the superficial materials which, here as in the North of Europe and America, may be designated as drift, cannot be the result of the decomposition of underlying rocks, since the latter are sometimes granite, sometimes gneiss, sometimes mica or talcose slate, sometimes sandstone, while the drift presents the same composition everywhere. I am as far as ever from being able to point out the origin of these materials and the direction of their transportation. Now that Major Coutinho has learned to distinguish the drift from the decomposed rocks, he assures me that we shall find it throughout the valley of the Amazons. The boldest imagination shrinks from any generalization on this subject, and yet we must gradually familiarize ourselves with the idea that the cause which has dispersed these materials, whatever it be, has acted on the largest scale, since they are probably to be found all over the continent. Already I learn that my young travelling companions have observed the drift in the environs of Barbacena and Ouro-Preto, and in the valley of the Rio das Velhas. My zoological results are not less satisfactory; and to speak of the fishes alone, I have found at Para during one week more species than have as yet been described from the whole basin of the Amazons—sixty-three in all. This study will be useful, I hope, to ichthyology, for I have already succeeded in distinguishing five new families and eighteen new genera, while the unpublished species do not number less than forty-nine. It is a guaranty of the rich harvest I shall make when I enter upon the domain of the Amazons properly so called; for I have seen as yet but a tenth part of the fluviatile species known from this basin, and some of the marine species which come up to Para. Unhappily, Mr. Burkhardt is ill, and has been able to paint but four of the new species we have procured; and of nearly half the number, only single specimens have been secured. On my return I must make a longer stay in Para in order to fill these deficiencies. I am enchanted with the grandeur of nature here. Your Majesty certainly reigns over the most beautiful empire of the world; and, personal as are the attentions which I receive wherever I stop, I cannot but believe that, were it not for the generous and hospitable character of the Brazilians and the interest of the higher classes in the progress of science and civilization, I should not have met with the facilities which crowd my path. Thus, in order to render the exploration of the river from Para to Manaos more easy, Mr. Pimenta Bueno, instead of allowing me to take the regular steamer, has put at my disposition, for a month or six weeks, one of the finest boats of the company, where I am installed as conveniently as in my Museum at Cambridge. Mr. Coutinho is full of attention, and renders my work doubly light by procuring, in advance, all the information possible. But I will not further abuse your Majesty's leisure, only begging you to believe in the complete devotion and respectful affection of

Your humble and obedient servant,
L. Agassiz

NOTES

1. The name consecrated by De Saussure to designate certain rocks in Switzerland which have had their surfaces rounded under the action of the glaciers. Their gently swelling outlines are thought to resemble sheep resting on the ground, and for this reason the people in the Alps call them *roches moutonnées*.

2. Bohn's edition of Humboldt's Personal Narrative, Chap. II. p. 134. Humboldt alludes to these formations repeatedly; it is true that he refers them to the ancient conglomerates of the Devonian age, but his description agrees so perfectly with what I have observed along

the banks of the Amazons and the Rio Negro that there can be no doubt he speaks of the same thing. He wrote at one time when many of the results of modern geology were unknown, and his explanation of the phenomena was then perfectly natural. The passage from which the few lines in the text are taken shows that these deposits extend even to the Llanos.

3. I am aware that Bates mentions having heard that at Obydos calcareous layers, thickly studded with marine shells, had been found interstratified with the clay, but he did not himself examine the strata. The Obydos shells are not marine, but are fresh-water Unios, greatly resembling Aviculas, Solens, and Arcas. Such would-be marine fossils have been brought to me from the shore opposite to Obydos, near Santarem, and I have readily recognized them for what they truly are—fresh-water shells of the family of Naiades. I have myself collected specimens of these shells in the clay-beds along the banks of the Solimoens, near Teffe, and might have mistaken them for fossils of that formation had I not known how Naiades burrow in the mud. Their resemblance to the marine genera mentioned above is very remarkable, and the mistake as to their true zoological character is as natural as that by which earlier ichthyologists, and even travellers of very recent date, have confounded some fresh-water fishes from the Upper Amazons, of the genus Pterophyllum (Heckel), with the marine genus Platax.

4. As I have stated in the beginning, I am satisfied that the unstratified clay deposit of Rio and its vicinity is genuine glacial drift, resulting from the grinding of the loose materials interposed between the glacier and the solid rock in place, and retaining to this day the position in which it was left by the ice. Like all such accumulations, it is totally free from stratification. If this be so, it is evident, on comparing the two formations, that the ochraceous sandy clay of the valley of the Amazons has been deposited under different circumstances; that, while it owes its resemblance to the Rio drift to the fact that its materials were originally ground by glaciers in the upper part of the valley, these materials have subsequently been spread throughout the whole basin and actually deposited under the agency of water. A survey of the more southern provinces of Brazil, extending to the temperate zone, where the combined effects of a tropical sun and of tropical rains must naturally be wanting, will, I trust, remove all the difficulties still attending this explanation. The glacial phenomena, with all their characteristic features, are already known to cover the southernmost parts of South America. The intervening range, between 22° and 36° of south latitude, cannot fail to exhibit the transition from

the drift of the cold and temperate zone to the formations of a kindred character described above from the tropical zone. The knowledge of these deposits will definitely settle the question; and either prove the correctness of my generalizations or show their absurdity. I feel no anxiety as to the result. I only long for a speedy removal of all doubts.

5. I would here remind the reader of the terraces of Glen Roy, which indicate successive reductions of the barrier encasing the lake, similar to those assumed to have taken place at the mouth of the Amazons.

6. Mr. Agassiz was indebted to Mr. Hitch for valuable additions to his collections, and for many acts of kindness in behalf of the expedition.

7. Here, as elsewhere, I found ready and willing coadjutors among amateur collectors. On my return from the Amazons, many months later, I found collections made in my absence by Dr. Mendes and Senhor Barroso, who had been our companions on board the steamer. At Parahyba do Norte I was indebted in the same way to Dr. Justa. These collections will afford invaluable materials for the comparison of the Coast Faunae.—L. A.

8. At a later period I owed to Dr. Braga far more than the ordinary courtesy extended to a stranger. I had informed him that Mr. St. John, then following the course of the Rio San Francisco, on his way to the province of Piauhy, would arrive in Maranham at the close of his journey. When he reached that city he was very seriously ill with fever. Dr. Braga took him into his house, where he was attended by him and his family as if he had been one of their kindred. I have, indeed, little doubt that my young friend owed his recovery to the considerate care with which he was treated under their kindly roof.—L. A.

9. These two Medusae belong to the Rhizostomidae, and I shall take an early opportunity to publish a description of them, with the drawing of Mr. Burkhardt.—L. A.

10. To Dr. Couto de Magalhaês Mr. Agassiz was indebted for unremitting attentions during our stay in the region of the Amazons. He never failed to facilitate the success of the expedition by every means in his power, and the large collections made under his directions during our sojourn upon the Upper Amazons were among the most valuable contributions to its scientific results. When he heard that Mr. Ward, one of our young companions, was coming down the Tocantins, he sent a boat and boatmen to meet him, and on his arrival in Para received him in his own house, where he remained his guest during his stay in the city.

11. This mushroom belongs to the genus Phallus, and seems to be an undescribed species. I preserved it in alcohol, but was unable to have any drawing made from it before its beauty and freshness were quite gone. In the early morning, while the grass was still damp, we often found a peculiar snail, a species of Bulimus, creeping by the roadside. The form of the anterior part of the foot was unlike that of any species known thus far from this group. Such facts show the desirableness of making drawings from the soft parts of these animals as well as from their solid envelopes.—L. A.

12. The President of this line is the Baron de Maza, esteemed by his countrymen as a financier of great ability and a man of rare energy, perseverance, and patriotism. As he was in Europe during the year of my visit to Brazil, I had not the pleasure of a personal acquaintance with him, and I therefore welcome this opportunity of thanking him for the liberality shown in all of their dealings with me by the company of which he is the moving spirit.—L. A.

III.

Clarities

Note

The precision of Agassiz's mind is the permanent quality that has refused to mellow into quaintness. A hundred years removed from his dissecting table, from his clarity in the classroom, we still have his words. Agassiz's best and most elegant descriptions are of things which tax language to describe: the anatomy of jellyfish, the inside of eggs. He had, with words alone, to be both sculptor and microscopist, and had to be these simultaneously. Discerning, distinguishing: a lifetime of study is behind these painstaking processes, in order that he know what he's looking at, and hundreds of hours of observation went to ascertain the accuracy of his perceptions.

The power to describe is only partially a linguistic one; to share a perception must be one of man's highest achievements, for the describer is always teaching us how to perceive in the very act of describing. He sees; he makes us see.

Here is a miniature collection of Agassizian perceptions: of a jellyfish, a turtle embryo, American autumn, the earth's oldest terrain, the American character, the evidence of glaciers. Each example is chosen to show the versatile adjustments of his mind in the act of perceiving. With equal facility he can discern the wrinkling of cell tissue or the wrinkling of the earth into a mountain chain; with stroboscopic precision he can analyze motion, whether the flicking of a fish's tail or the slow transmutation of a coastline over millions of years.

III. Clarities

Cyanea Arctica

Seen floating in the water Cyanea Arctica exhibits a large circular disk, of a substance not unlike jelly, thick in the centre, and suddenly thinning out towards the edge, which presents several indentations. The centre of that disk is of a dark purplish-brown color, while the edge is much lighter, almost white and transparent. This disk is constantly heaving and falling, at regular intervals; the margin is especially active, so much so, that, at times, it is stretched on a level with the whole surface of the disk, which, in such a condition, is almost flat, while, at other times, it is so fully arched that it assumes the appearance of a hemisphere. These motions recall so strongly those of an umbrella, alternately opened and shut, that writers, who have described similar animals, have generally called this gelatinous disk the umbrella. From the lower surface of this disk hang, conspicuously, three kinds of appendages. Near the margin there are eight bunches of long tentacles, moving in every direction, sometimes extending to an enormous length, sometimes shortened to a mere coil of entangled threads, constantly rising and falling, stretching now in one direction and then in another, but generally spreading slantingly in a direction opposite to that of the onward movement of the animal. These streamers may be compared to floating tresses of hair, encircling organs which are farther inward upon the lower surface of the disk. Of these organs, there are also eight bunches, which alternate with the eight bunches of tentacles, but they are of two kinds; four are elegant sacks, adorned, as it were, with waving ruffles projecting in large clusters, which are alternately pressed forward and withdrawn, and might also be compared to bunches of grapes, by turns inflated and collapsed. These four bunches alternate with four masses of folds, hanging like rich curtains, loosely waving to and fro, and as they wave, extending

177

downwards, or shortening rapidly, recalling, to those who have
had an opportunity of witnessing the phenomenon, the play of
the streamers of an aurora borealis. All these parts have their fixed
position; they are held together by a sort of horizontal curtain,
which is suspended from the lower surface of the gelatinous disk.
The horizontal curtain is itself connected with the disk, fastened
to it as it were by ornamental stitches, which divide the whole
field into a number of areas, alternately larger and smaller, now
concentric, now radiating, between which the organs already
described are inserted.

—*Contributions to the Natural History of the*
United States, 1862

Character

Neu-Wied quotes as a remarkable fact, that the Chelonara
serpentina bites as soon as it is hatched. I have seen it snapping
in the same fierce manner as it does when full-grown, at a time
it was a pale, almost colorless embryo, wrapped up in its foetal
envelopes, with a yolk larger than itself hanging from its ster-
num, three months before hatching.

—Note to the *Essay on Classification,* 1857

The Ripening of Leaves

It was late in September, just at the turn of the leaf; the
woods were in all their golden and crimson glory, with here and
there a purple beech, or a background of dark green pines. Familiar as we all are with the brilliancy of the autumnal foliage in
the neighborhood of our towns, one must see it in the unbroken

forest, covering the country with rainbow hues as far as the eye
can reach, in order to appreciate fully its wonderful beauty. A
few words on this change of color, which is as constant as any
other botanical character (each kind of tree having its special
tints peculiar to itself, and not reproduced by other kinds), may
not be amiss. Indeed, not only does every species have its appointed range of color, but each individual tree has its history
told more or less distinctly in the ripening of the foliage. A weaker
or a younger limb may have put on its autumnal garb, and be
almost ready to drop its leaves, while the rest of the tree is un-
touched. A single scarlet maple or red oak often gives us the most
beautiful arrangement of tints, from the green of midsummer,
through every shade of orange and red; in the same way one leaf
may ripen unequally, its green surface being barred or spotted
with crimson or gold for days before the whole leaf turns. These
differences give ample opportunity for studying the ripening
process. In attempting to determine the cause of these changes,
it ought not to be forgotten that they occur locally, and also make
their appearance on particular trees much earlier than upon
others; so early, indeed, as to show clearly the fallacy of the prev-
alent idea that they are caused by frost. The temperature remains ten or fifteen degrees above the freezing-point for a month
and more after a good many of our trees have assumed
their bright autumnal hues. The process is, no doubt, akin to
that of the ripening of fruits: especially in such fleshy fruits as
turn from green to yellow, purple, or red, like apples, peaches,
plums, cherries, and others. The change in color coincides with
changes in the constitutional chemical elements of the plant; and
this comparison between the ripening of foliage and fruit seems
the more natural, when we remember that fruits are but a modification of leaves, assuming higher functions and special adaptations in the flower, so as to produce what we call a fruit. The
ripening process by which the leaves take on their final colors is
as constant and special as in the fruits. The cherries do not assume their various shades of red, deepening sometimes into black,
or the plums their purples, or the peaches their velvety-rose tints,
or the apples their greens, russets, browns, and reds, with more
unvarying accuracy than the different kinds of maples and oaks,

or the beeches, birches, and ashes, take on their characteristic tints. The inequality of the ripening of the foliage alluded to above has also its counterpart in the fruits. Here and there a single apple or peach or pear ripens prematurely, while all the rest of the fruit remains green, or a separate branch brings its harvest to maturity in advance of all the surrounding branches. No doubt the brilliancy of the change in the United States, as compared with other countries, is partly due to the dryness of the climate; and indeed it has been observed that certain European flowers take on deeper hues when transplanted in America. But I believe the cause lies rather in the special character of certain American plants and trees. The Virginia-creeper, for instance, which is much cultivated now in France and Germany, turns to as brilliant a scarlet in a European garden as in its native woods.

—*Geological Sketches*, Second Series, 1876

The Laurentian Hills

There is, perhaps, no part of the world, certainly none familiar to science, where the early geological periods can be studied with so much ease and precision as in the United States. Along their northern borders, between Canada and the United States, there runs the low line of hills known as the Laurentian Hills. Insignificant in height, nowhere rising more than fifteen hundred or two thousand feet above the level of the sea, these are nevertheless the first mountains that broke the uniform level of the earth's surface and lifted themselves above the waters. Their low stature, as compared with that of other more lofty mountain-ranges, is in accordance with an invariable rule, by which the relative age of mountains may be estimated. The oldest mountains are the lowest, while the younger and more recent ones tower above their elders, and are usually more torn and dislocated also. This is easily understood, when we remember that all mountains and mountain-chains are the result of upheavals, and

that the violence of the outbreak must have been in proportion
to the strength of the resistance. When the crust of the earth was
so thin that the heated masses within easily broke through it,
they were not thrown to so great a height, and formed comparatively low elevations, such as the Canadian hills or the mountains
of Bretagne [Britanny] and Wales. But in later times, when
young, vigorous giants, such as the Alps, the Himalayas, or, later
still, the Rocky Mountains, forced their way out from their fiery
prison house, the crust of the earth was much thicker, and fearful
indeed must have been the convulsions which attended their exit.

The Laurentian Hills form, then, a granite range, stretching
from Eastern Canada to the Upper Mississippi, and immediately
along its base are gathered the Azoic deposits, the first stratified
beds in which the absence of life need not surprise us, since they
were formed beneath a heated ocean. As well might we expect
to find the remains of fish or shells or crabs at the bottom of gey-
sers or of boiling springs, as on those early shores bathed by an
ocean of which the heat must have been so intense. Although,
from the condition in which we find it, this first granite range has
evidently never been disturbed by any violent convulsion since
its first upheaval, yet there has been a gradual rising of that part
of the continent, for the Azoic beds do not lie horizontally along
the base of the Laurentian Hills in the position in which they
must originally have been deposited, but are lifted and rest
against their slopes. They have been more or less dislocated in
this process, and are greatly metamorphized by the intense heat
to which they must have been exposed. Indeed, all the oldest
stratified rocks have been baked by the prolonged action of heat.

It may be asked how the materials for those first stratified
deposits were provided. In later times, when an abundant and
various soil covered the earth, when every river brought down to
the ocean, not only its yearly tribute of mud or clay or lime, but
the *débris* of animals and plants that lived and died in its waters
or along its banks, when every lake and pond deposited at its
bottom in successive layers the lighter or heavier materials floating in its waters and settling gradually beneath them, the process
by which stratified materials are collected and gradually harden
into rock is more easily understood. But when the solid surface

of the earth was only just beginning to form, it would seem that the floating matter in the sea can hardly have been in sufficient quantity to form any extensive deposits. No doubt there was some abrasion even of that first crust; but the more abundant source of the earliest stratification is to be found in the submarine volcanoes that poured their liquid streams into the first ocean. At what rate these materials would be so deposited in layers is evident from the relative position of the earliest rocks. I have already spoken of the innumerable chimneys perforating the Azoic beds, narrow outlets of Plutonic rock, protruding through the earliest strata. Not only are such funnels filled with the crystalline mass of granite that flowed through them in a liquid state, but it has often poured over their sides, mingling with the stratified beds around. In the present state of our knowledge, we can explain such appearances only by supposing that the heated materials within the earth's crust poured out frequently, meeting little resistance—that they then scattered and were precipitated in the ocean around, settling in successive strata at its bottom—that through such strata the heated masses within continued to pour again and again, forming for themselves the chimney-like outlets above mentioned.

Such, then, was the earliest American land—a long, narrow island, almost continental in its proportions, since it stretched from the eastern borders of Canada nearly to the point where now the base of the Rocky Mountains meets the plain of the Mississippi Valley. We may still walk along its ridge and know that we tread upon the ancient granite that first divided the waters into a northern and southern ocean; and if our imaginations will carry us so far, we may look down toward its base and fancy how the sea washed against this earliest shore of a lifeless world. This is no romance, but the bald, simple truth; for the fact that this granite band was lifted out of the waters so early in the history of the world, and has not since been submerged, has, of course, prevented any subsequent deposits from forming above it. And this is true of all the northern part of the United States. It has been lifted gradually, the beds deposited in one period being subsequently raised, and forming a shore along which those of the succeeding one collected, so that we have their whole sequence before us. In regions where all the geological deposits, Silurian, Devonian, Carboniferous, Permian, Triassic, etc., are piled one upon another, and we can get a glimpse of their internal relations only where some rent has laid them open, or where their ragged edges, worn away by the abrading action of external influences, expose to view their successive layers, it must, of course, be more difficult to follow their connection. For this reason the American continent offers facilities to the geologist denied to him in the so-called Old World, where the earlier deposits are comparatively hidden, and the broken character of the land, intersected by mountains in every direction, renders his investigation still more difficult. Of course, when I speak of the geological deposits as so completely unveiled to us here, I do not forget the sheet of drift which covers the continent from North to South, and which we shall discuss hereafter, when I reach that part of my subject. But the drift is only a superficial and recent addition to the soil, resting loosely above the other geological deposits, and arising, as we shall see, from very different causes.

—*Geological Sketches*, First Series, 1866

On the Americans

Question upon question greets me regarding the new world, on the shore of which I have just landed, and yet about which I have so much to say that I fear to tire my listeners.

Naturalist as I am, I cannot but put the people first—the people who have opened this part of the American continent to European civilization. What a people! But to understand them you must live among them. Our education, the principles of our society, the motives of our actions, differ so greatly from what I see here, that I should try in vain to give you an idea of this great nation, passing from childhood to maturity with the faults of spoiled children, and yet with the nobility of character and the enthusiasm of youth. Their look is wholly turned toward the future; their social life is not yet irrevocably bound to exacting antecedents, and thus nothing holds them back, unless, perhaps, a consideration for the opinion in which they may be held in Europe. This deference toward England (unhappily, to them, Europe means almost exclusively England) is a curious fact in the life of the American people. They know us but little, even after having made a tour in France, or Italy, or Germany. From England they receive their literature, and the scientific work of central Europe reaches them through English channels. . . . Notwithstanding this kind of dependence upon England, in which American savants have voluntarily placed themselves, I have formed a high opinion of their acquirements, since I have learned to know them better, and I think we should render a real service to them and to science, by freeing them from this tutelage, raising them in their own eyes, and drawing them also a little more toward ourselves. Do not think that these remarks are prompted by the least antagonism toward English savants, whom no one more than myself has reason to regard with affection and esteem. But since these men are so worthy to soar on their own wings, why not help them to take flight? They need only confidence, and some special recognition from Europe would tend to give them this. . . .

Among the zoologists of this country I would place Mr. Dana at the head. He is still very young, fertile in ideas, rich in facts, equally able as geologist and mineralogist. When his work on corals is completed, you can better judge of him. One of these days you will make him a correspondent of the Institute, unless he kills himself with work too early, or is led away by his tendency to generalization. Then there is Gould, author of the malacologic fauna of Massachusetts, and who is now working up the mollusks of the Wilkes Expedition. De Kay and Lea, whose works have long been known, are rather specialists, I should say. I do not yet know Holbrook personally. Pickering, of the Wilkes Expedition, is a well of science, perhaps the most erudite naturalist here. Haldeman knows the fresh-water gasteropods of this country admirably well, and has published a work upon them. Le Conte is a critical entomologist who seems to me thoroughly familiar with what is doing in Europe. In connection with Haldeman he is working up the articulates of the Wilkes Expedition. Wyman, recently made professor at Cambridge, is an excellent comparative anatomist, and the author of several papers on the organization of fishes. . . . The botanists are less numerous, but Asa Gray and Dr. Torrey are known wherever the study of botany is pursued. Gray, with indefatigable zeal, will gain upon his competitors. . . . The geologists and mineralogists form the most numerous class among the savants of the country. The fact that every state has its corps of official geologists has tended to develop study in this direction to the detriment of other branches, and will later, I fear, tend to the detriment of science itself; for the utilitarian tendency thus impressed on the work of American geologists will retard their progress. With us, on the contrary, researches of this kind tend to assume a more and more scientific character. Still, the body of American geologists forms, as a whole, a most respectable contingent. The names of Charles T. Jackson, James Hall, Hitchcock, Henry and William Rogers (two brothers), have long been familiar to European science. After the geologists, I would mention Dr. Morton, of Philadelphia, well known as the author of several papers upon fossils, and still better by his great work upon the indigenous races of America. He is a man of science in the best sense; admirable both as regards his knowledge and his activity. He is the pillar of the Philadelphia Academy.

The chemists and physicists, again, form another utilitarian class of men in this country. As with many of them purely scientific work is not their sole object, it is difficult for an outsider to distinguish between the clever manipulators and those who have higher aims. . . .

The mathematicians have also their *culte*, dating back to Bowditch, the translator of the "Mécanique céleste," and the author of a work on practical navigation. He died in Boston, where they are now erecting a magnificent monument to his memory. Mr. Peirce, professor at Cambridge, is considered here the equal of our great mathematicians. It is not for me, who cannot do a sum in addition, to pretend to judgment in the matter.

You are familiar, no doubt, with the works of Captain Wilkes and the report of his journey around the world. His charts are much praised. The charts of the coasts and harbors of the United States, made under the direction of Dr. Bache and published at government expense, are admirable. The reports of Captain Frémont concerning his travels are also most interesting and instructive; to botanists especially so, on account of the scientific notes accompanying them.

—Letter to Milne Edwards, May 31, 1847

Rocks Like Flocks of Sheep

Among the inequalities of the glacier-worn surfaces which deserve special notice are the so-called *roches moutonnées*. They are knolls of a peculiar appearance, frequent in the Alps, and first noticed by the illustrious De Saussure, who designated them by that name, because, where they are numerous and seen from a distance, they resemble the rounded backs of a flock of sheep resting on the ground. These knolls are the result of the prolonged abrasion of masses of rocks separated by deep indentations wide enough to be filled up by large glaciers, overtopping the summits of the intervening prominences, and passing over them like a river, or like tide-currents flowing over a submerged ledge of rock. It is evident that water rushing over such sunken hills or ledges, adapting itself readily to all the inequalities over which it flows, and forming eddies against the obstacles in its course, will scoop out tortuous furrows upon the bottom, and hollow out rounded cavities against the walls, acting especially along the pre-existing fissures and upon the softer parts of the rock. The glacier, on the contrary, moving as a solid mass, and carrying on its under side its gigantic file set in a fine paste, will in course of time abrade uniformly the angles against which it strikes, equalize the depressions between the prominent masses, and round them off until they present those smooth bulging knolls known as the *roches moutonnées* in the Alps, and so characteristic everywhere of glacier-action. A comparison of any tide-worn hum-

mock with such a glacier-worn mound will convince the observer
that its smooth and evenly rounded surface was never produced
by water.

Beside their peculiar form, the *roches moutonnées* present
all the characteristic features of glacier-action in all their polished
surfaces accompanied with the straight lines, grooves, and furrows above described. There are two circumstances connected
with these knolls deserving special notice. They frequently
present the glacial marks only on one side, while the opposite
side has all the irregularities and roughness of a hill-slope not
acted upon by ice. It is evident that the polished side was the one
turned towards the advancing glacier, the side against which the
ice pressed in its onward movement—while it passed over the
other side, the lee side as we may call it, without coming in immediate contact with it, bridging the depression and touching
bottom again a little farther on. As an additional evidence of this
fact, we frequently find on the lee side of such knolls accumulations of the loose materials which the glacier carries with it. It is
only, however, when the knolls are quite high, and abrupt enough
to allow any rigid substance to bridge over the space in its descent from the summit to the surface below, that we find these
conditions; when the knolls are low and slope gently downward in every direction, they present the characteristic glacier-
surfaces equally on all sides. This circumstance should be borne
in mind by all who investigate the traces of glacier-action; for the
inequality in the surfaces presented by the opposite sides of any
obstacle in the path of ice is often an important means of determining the direction of its motion.

The other characteristic peculiarity of these *roches moutonnées* consists in the direction of the glacier-scratches which
ascend the slope to its summit in a direct line on one side, while
they deviate to the right and left on the other sides of the knoll,
more or less obliquely according to its steepness. Occasionally,
large boulders may be found perched on the very summit of such
prominences. Their position is inexplicable by the supposition of
currents as the cause of their transportation. Any current strong
enough to carry a boulder to such a height would of course sweep
it on with it. This phenomenon finds, however, an easy explana-

tion in the glacial theory. The thickness of such a sheet of ice is of course less above such a hill or mound than over the lower levels adjoining it. Not only will the ice melt, therefore, more readily at this spot, but, as ice is transparent to heat, the summit of the prominence will become warmed by the rays of the sun, and will itself facilitate the melting of the ice above it. On the breaking up of the ice, therefore, such a spot will be the first to yield, and allow the boulders carried on the back of the glacier to fall into the hollow thus formed, where they will rest upon the projecting rock left uncovered. This is no theoretical explanation; there are such cases in Switzerland, where holes in the ice are formed immediately above the summit of hills or prominences over which the glacier passes, and into which it drops its burdens. Of course, where the ice is constantly renewed over such a spot by the onward progress of the glacier, these materials may be carried off again; but if we suppose such a case to occur at the breaking up of the glacier-period, in a locality from which the ice was disappearing forever, it is easy to account for the poising of these large boulders on prominent peaks or ledges.

The appearances about the *roches moutonnées*, especially the straight scratches and grooves on the side up which the ice ascended, have led to a mistaken view of the mode in which large boulders are transported by ice. It has been supposed by those who, while they accepted the glacial theory, were not wholly conversant with the mode of action of glaciers, that, in passing through the bottom of a valley, for instance, the glacier would take up large boulders, and, carrying them along with it, would push them up such a slope and deposit them on its summit. It is true that large boulders may sometimes be found in front of glaciers among the materials of their terminal moraines, and may upon any advance of the glacier be pushed forward by it. But I know of no example of erratic boulders being carried to considerable distances and raised from lower to higher levels by this means. All the angular boulders perched upon prominent rocks must have fallen upon the surface of the glacier in the upper part of its course, where rocky ledges rise above its surface and send down their broken fragments. The surface of any boulder carried under the ice, or pushed along for any distance at its terminus,

would show the friction and pressure to which it had been sub-
jected. In this connection it should be remembered that in the
case of large glaciers low hills form no obstacle to their onward
progress, especially when the glacier is thick enough to cover
them completely, and even to rise far above them. The *roches
moutonnées* about the Grimsel show that hills many hundred
feet high have been passed over by the great glacier of the Aar,
when it descended as far as Meyringen, without having seemingly
influenced its onward progress.

—*Geological Sketches*, Second Series, 1876

IV.

Agassiz the Lecturer

Two public lectures that became chapters
in *Methods of Study in Natural History*

Note

Agassiz the teacher—the only identification he allowed on his tombstone—taught not only his colleagues and students but the public as well. It was as a lecturer that he came to America, and his wide popularity as a celebrated figure derived from his lectures and magazine articles. Nor did Agassiz consider these drudgery. He accepted it as part of his duty as a learned man to guide the young into his own polymathy, to prepare textbooks, to inspire, to explain natural design explicitly and engagingly. As he spoke he chalked diagrams on a blackboard, and the deftness with which he drew is said to have been breathtaking.

The two pieces which follow are public lectures. They were delivered at the Lowell Institute in Boston, without text, and one suspects, without notes. "Notes were, however, taken of them at the time," Agassiz explains in the book which they eventually became, *Methods of Study in Natural History*, "and I very willingly assented to the suggestion of some of my listeners, that they should be recorded in the form of articles for the *Atlantic Monthly*." In 1863 the fifteen lectures made a concise textbook. A sixteenth chapter, "Embryology and Classification," was "especially addressed to the professional naturalist." Otherwise the book was tempered to "the mind of a popular audience."

A quarter of a century after Agassiz's death Houghton Mifflin's book list carried as stock items the two series of *Geological Sketches* (the second posthumous), the *Methods of Study*, and *A Journey in Brazil*, together with Elizabeth Cary Agassiz's *Life and Correspondence*.

In an age of Chautauqua and Lyceum lectures Agassiz ranked among the finest of the spellbinders, and his name still lives beyond libraries and academies in traditional memory, for his brilliance as a speaker. Something of the brilliant explicator's voi e can still be detected in the written word.

IV. Agassiz the Lecturer

Methods of Study in Natural History

CHAPTER II. *Nomenclature and Classification.*

Proceeding upon the view that there is a close analogy between the way in which every individual student penetrates into Nature and the progress of science as a whole in the history of humanity, I continue my sketch of the successive steps that have led to our present state of knowledge. I began with Aristotle, and showed that this great philosopher, though he prepared a digest of all the knowledge belonging to his time, yet did not feel the necessity of any system or of any scientific language differing from the common mode of expression of his day. He presents his information as a man with his eyes open narrates in a familiar style what he sees. As civilization spread and science had its representatives in other countries besides Greece, it became indispensable to have a common scientific language, a technical nomenclature, combining many objects under common names, and enabling every naturalist to express the results of his observations readily and simply in a manner intelligible to all other students of Natural History.

Linnaeus devised such a system, and to him we owe a most simple and comprehensive scientific mode of designating animals and plants. It may at first seem no advantage to give up the common names of the vernacular and adopt the unfamiliar ones, but a word of explanation will make the object clear. Perceiving, for instance, the close relations between certain members of the larger groups, Linnaeus gave to them names that should be common to all, and which are called generic names—as we speak of Ducks, when we would designate in one word the Mallard, the Widgeon, the Canvas-Back, etc.; but to these generic names he added qualifying epithets, called specific names, to indicate the different kinds in each group. For example, the Lion, the Tiger, the Panther, the Domestic Cat constitute such a natural group, which Linnaeus called *Felis*, Cat, indicating the whole genus; but the species he designates as *Felis catus*, the Domestic Cat— *Felis leo*, the Lion—*Felis tigris*, the Tiger—*Felis panthera*, the Panther. So he called all the Dogs *Canis;* but for the different kinds we have *Canis familiaris*, the Domestic Dog—*Canis lupus*, the Wolf—*Canis vulpes*, the Fox, etc.

In some families of the vegetable kingdom we can appreciate better the application of this nomenclature, because we have something corresponding to it in the vernacular. We have, for instance, one name for all the Oaks, but we call the different kinds Swamp Oak, Red Oak, White Oak, Chestnut Oak, etc. So Linnaeus, in his botanical nomenclature, called all the Oaks by the generic name *Quercus* (characterizing them by their fruit, the acorn, common to all), and qualified them as *Quercus bicolor, Quercus rubra, Quercus alba, Quercus castanea*, etc., etc. His nomenclature, being so easy of application, became at once exceedingly popular, and made him the great scientific legislator of his century. He insisted on Latin names, because, if every naturalist should use his own language, it must lead to great confusion, and this Latin nomenclature of double significance was adopted by all. Another advantage of this binominal Latin nomenclature consists in preventing the confusion frequently arising from the use of the same name to designate different animals in different parts of the world—as, for instance, the name of Robin, used in America to designate a bird of the Thrush family, which is entirely different from the Robin of the Old World, one of the warblers—or of different names for the same animal, as Perch or Chogset or Burgall for our Cunner. Nothing is more to be deprecated than an over-appreciation of technicalities, valuing the name more highly than the thing; but some knowledge of this scientific nomenclature is necessary to every student of Nature.

While Linnaeus pointed out classes, orders, genera, and species, other naturalists had detected other divisions among animals, called families. Lamarck, who had been a distinguished botanist before he began his study of the animal kingdom, brought to his zoological researches his previous methods of investigation. Families in the vegetable kingdom had long been distinguished by French botanists; and one cannot examine the groups they call by this name, without perceiving, that, though they bring them together and describe them according to other characters, they have been unconsciously led to unite them from the general similarity of their port and bearing. Take, for instance, the families of Pines, Oaks, Beeches, Maples, etc., and you feel at once, that, besides the common characters given in the technical descriptions of these different groups of trees, there is also a general resemblance among them that would naturally lead us to associate them together, even if we knew nothing of the special features of their structure. By an instinctive recognition of this family likeness between plants, botanists have been led to seek for structural characters on which to unite them, and the groups so founded generally correspond with the combinations suggested by their appearance.

By a like process Lamarck combined animals into families. His method was adopted by French naturalists generally, and found favor especially with Cuvier, who was particularly successful in limiting families among animals, and in naming them happily, generally selecting names expressive of the features on which the groups were founded, or borrowing them from familiar animals. Much, indeed, depends upon the pleasant sound and the significance of a name; for an idea reaches the mind more easily when well expressed, and Cuvier's names were both simple and significant. His descriptions are also remarkable for their graphic precision—giving all that is essential, omitting all that is merely accessory. He has given us the keynote to his progress in his own expressive language:—

Je dus donc, et cette obligation me prit un temps considérable, je dus faire marcher de front l'anatomie et la zoologie, les dissections et le classement; chercher dans mes premières remarques sur l'organisation des distributions meilleures; m'en servir pour arriver à des remarques nouvelles; employer encore ces remarques à perfectionner les distributions; faire sortir enfin de cette fécondation mutuelle des deux sciences, l'une par l'autre, un système zoologique propre à servir d'introducteur et de guide dans le champ de l'anatomie, et un corps de doctrine anatomique propre à servir de développement et d'explication au système zoologique.*

It is deeply to be lamented that so many naturalists have entirely overlooked this significant advice of Cuvier's, with respect to combining zoological and anatomical studies in order to arrive at a clearer perception of the true affinities among animals. To sum it up in one word, he tells us that the secret of his method is "comparison,"—ever comparing and comparing throughout the enormous range of his knowledge of the organization of animals, and founding upon the differences as well as the similarities those broad generalizations under which he has included all animal structures. And this method, so prolific in his hands, has also a lesson for us all. In this country there is a growing interest in the study of Nature; but while there exist hundreds of elementary works illustrating the native animals of Europe, there are few such books here to satisfy the demand for information respecting the animals of our land and waters. We are thus forced to turn more and more to our own investigations and less to authority; and the true method of obtaining independent knowledge is this very method of Cuvier's—comparison.

Let us make the most common application of it to natural objects. Suppose we see together a Dog, a Cat, a Bear, a Horse, a Cow, and a Deer. The first feature that strikes us as common to any two of them is the horn in the Cow and Deer. But how shall we associate either of the others with these? We examine the teeth, and find those of the Dog, the Cat, and the Bear sharp and cutting, while those of the Cow, the Deer, and the Horse have flat surfaces, adapted to grinding and chewing, rather than cutting and tearing. We compare these features of their structure with the habits of these animals, and find that the first are carnivorous,

* "I therefore felt myself obliged, and this obligation cost me no little time, to make my studies in anatomy and zoology, dissection and classification, keep pace with each other; to seek in my earlier investigations upon organization a better distribution of groups; to employ these again as a means of perfecting my classification; to arrive in short, by this mutual fecundation of the two sciences at a zoological system which might serve as a pioneer and guide in the field of anatomy, and an anatomical method which would aid in the development and explanation of the zoological system."

that they seize and tear their prey, while the others are herbivorous or grazing animals, living only on vegetable substances, which they chew and grind. We compare further the Horse and Cow, and find that the Horse has front teeth both in the upper and lower jaw, while the Cow has them only in the lower; and going still further, and comparing the internal with the external features, we find this arrangement of the teeth in direct relation to the different structure of the stomach in the two animals—the Cow having a stomach with four pouches, adapted to a mode of digestion by which the food is prepared for the second mastication, while the Horse has a simple stomach. Comparing the Cow and the Deer, we find that the digestive apparatus is the same in both; but though they both have horns, in the Cow the horn is hollow, and remains through life firmly attached to the bone, while in the Deer it is solid and is shed every year. With these facts before us, we cannot hesitate to place the Dog, the Cat, and the Bear in one division, as carnivorous animals, and the other three in another division as herbivorous animals—and looking a little further, we perceive, that, in common with the Cow and the Deer, the Goat and the Sheep have cloven feet, and that they are all ruminants, while the Horse has a single hoof, does not ruminate, and must therefore be separated from them, even though, like them, he is herbivorous.

This is but the simplest illustration, taken from the most familiar objects, of this comparative method; but the same process is equally applicable to the most intricate problems in animal structures, and will give us the clew to all true affinities between animals. The education of a naturalist now consists chiefly in learning how to compare. If he have any power of generalization, when he has collected his facts, this habit of mental comparison will lead him up to principles, and to the great laws of combination. It must not discourage us, that the process is a slow and laborious one, and the results of one lifetime after all very small. It might seem invidious, were I to show here how small is the sum total of the work accomplished even by the great exceptional men, whose names are known throughout the civilized world. But I may at least be permitted to speak disparagingly of my own efforts, and to sum up in the fewest words the result of my life's work. I have devoted my whole life to the study of Nature, and yet a single sentence may express all that I have done. I have shown that there is a correspondence between the succession of Fishes in geological times and the different stages of their growth in the egg—this is all. It chanced to be a result that was found to apply to other groups and has led to other conclusions of a like nature but, such as it is, it has been reached by this system of comparison, which, though I speak of it now in its application to the study of Natural History, is equally important in every other branch of knowledge. By the same process the most mature results of scientific research in Philology, in Ethnology, and in Physical Science are reached. And let me say that the community should foster the purely intellectual efforts of scientific men as carefully as they do their elementary schools and their practical institutions, generally considered so much more useful and important to the public. For from what other source shall we derive the higher results that are gradually woven into the practical resources of our life, except from the researches of those very men who study science, not for its uses, but for its truth? It is this that gives it its noblest interest: it must be for truth's sake, and not even for the sake of its usefulness to humanity, that the scientific man studies Nature. The application of science to the useful arts requires other abilities, other qualities, other tools than his; and therefore I say that the man of science who follows his studies into their practical application is false to his calling. The practical man stands ever ready to take up the work where the scientific man leaves it, and to adapt it to the material wants and uses of daily life.

The publication of Cuvier's proposition, that the animal kingdom is built on four plans, however imperfectly understood and appreciated at first, created, nevertheless, an extraordinary excitement throughout the scientific world. All naturalists proceeded to test it, and some among them soon recognized in it a great scientific truth—while others, who thought more of making themselves prominent than of advancing science, proposed poor amendments, that were sure to be rejected on further investigation. Some of these criticisms and additions, however, were truly improvements, and touched upon points overlooked by Cuvier.

Blainville, especially, took up the element of form among animals—whether divided on two sides, whether radiated, whether irregular, etc. He, however, made the mistake of giving very elaborate names to animals already known under simpler ones. Why, for instance, call all animals with parts radiating in every direction *Actinomorpha* or *Actinozoaria,* when they had received the significant name of *Radiates?* It seemed to be a new system, when in fact it was only a new name. Ehrenberg, likewise, made an important distinction, when he united the animals according to the difference in their nervous systems; but he also encumbered the nomenclature unnecessarily, when he added to the names *Anaima* and *Enaima* of Aristotle those of *Myeloneura* and *Ganglioneura.*

But it is not my object to give all the classifications of different authors here, and I will therefore pass over many noted ones, as those of Burmeister, Milne-Edwards, Siebold and Stannius, Owen, Leuckart, Vogt, Van Beneden, and others, and proceed to give some account of one investigator who did as much for the progress of Zoology as Cuvier, though he is comparatively little known among us.

Karl Ernst von Baer proposed a classification based, like Cuvier's, upon plan; but he recognized what Cuvier failed to perceive—namely, the importance of distinguishing between type (by which he means exactly what Cuvier means by plan) and complication of structure—in other words, between plan and the execution of the plan. He recognized four types, which correspond exactly to Cuvier's four plans, though he calls them by different names. Let us compare them.

CUVIER	BAER
Radiates	Peripheric
Mollusks	Massive
Articulates	Longitudinal
Vertebrates	Doubly Symmetrical

Though perhaps less felicitous, the names of Baer express the same ideas as those of Cuvier. By the *Peripheric* type he signified those animals in which all the parts converge from the periphery or circumference of the animal to its centre. Cuvier only reverses this definition in his name of *Radiates*, signifying the animals in which all parts radiate from the centre to the circumference. By *Massive*, Baer indicated those animals in which the body is undivided, soft and concentrated, without a very distinct individualization of parts—exactly the animals included by Cuvier under his name of *Mollusks*, or soft-bodied animals. In his selection of the epithet *Longitudinal*, Baer was less fortunate; for all animals have a longitudinal diameter, and this word was not therefore, sufficiently special. Yet his *Longitudinal* type answers exactly to Cuvier's *Articulates*—animals in which all parts are arranged in a succession of articulated joints along a longitudinal axis. Cuvier has expressed this jointed structure in the name *Articulates;* whereas Baer, in his name of *Longitudinal*, referred only to the arrangement of joints in longitudinal succession, in a continuous string, as it were, one after another, indicating thus the prevalence of length as the predominant diameter of the body. For the *Doubly Symmetrical* type his name is the better of the two, since Cuvier's name of *Vertebrates* alludes only to the backbone—while Baer, who is an embryologist, signifies in his their mode of growth also. He knew what Cuvier did not know, when he first proposed his classification: that in its first formation the germ of the Vertebrate divides in two folds; one turning up above the backbone, to form and enclose all the sensitive organs —the spinal marrow, the organs of sense, all those organs by which life is expressed; the other turning down below the backbone, and enclosing all those organs by which life is maintained —the organs of digestion, of respiration, of circulation, of reproduction, etc. So there is in this type not only an equal division of parts on either side, but also a division above and below, making thus a double symmetry in the plan, expressed by Baer in the name he gave it. Baer was perfectly original in his conception of these four types, for his paper was published in the very same year with that of Cuvier. But even in Germany, his native land, his ideas were not fully appreciated: strange that it should be so —for had his countrymen recognized his genius, they might have earlier claimed him as the compeer of the great French naturalist.

Baer also founded the science of Embryology, under the guidance of his teacher, Döllinger. His researches in this direction showed him that animals were not only built on four plans, but that they grew according to four modes of development. The Vertebrate arises from the egg differently from the Articulate— the Articulate differently from the Mollusk—the Mollusk differently from the Radiate. Cuvier only showed us the four plans as they exist in the adult; Baer went a step further, and showed us the four plans in the process of formation.

But his greatest scientific achievement is perhaps the discovery that all animals originate from eggs, and that all these eggs are at first identical in substance and structure. The wonderful and untiring research condensed into this simple statement, that all animals arise from eggs, and that all those eggs are identical in the beginning, may well excite our admiration. This egg consists of an outer envelope, the vitelline membrane, containing a fluid more or less dense, and variously colored, the yolk; within this is a second envelope, the so-called germinative vesicle, containing a somewhat different and more transparent fluid, and in the fluid of this second envelope float one or more so-called germinative specks. At this stage of their growth all eggs are microscopically small, yet each one has such tenacity of its individual principle of life that no egg was ever known to swerve from the pattern of the parent animal that gave it birth.

CHAPTER III. *Categories of Classification.*

From the time that Linnaeus showed us the necessity of a scientific system as a framework for the arrangement of scientific facts in Natural History, the number of divisions adopted by zoologists and botanists increased steadily. Not only were families, orders, and classes added to genera and species, but these were further multiplied by subdivisions of the different groups. But as the number of divisions increased, they lost in precise meaning, and it became more and more doubtful how far they were true to Nature. Moreover, these divisions were not taken in the same sense by all naturalists: what were called families by some were called orders by others, while the orders of some were the classes of others, till it began to be doubted whether these scientific systems had any foundation in Nature, or signified anything more than that it had pleased Linnaeus, for instance, to call certain groups of animals by one name, while Cuvier had chosen to call them by another.

These divisions are, first, the most comprehensive groups, the primary divisions, called branches by some, types by others, and divided by some naturalists into so-called sub-types, meaning only a more limited circumscription of the same kind of group; next we have classes, and these also have been divided into sub-classes; then orders and sub-orders; families and sub-families or tribes; then genera, species, and varieties. With reference to the question whether these groups really exist in Nature, or are merely the expression of individual theories and opinions, it is worth while to study the works of the early naturalists, in order to trace the natural process by which scientific classification has been reached; for in this, as in other departments of learning, practice has always preceded theory. We do the thing before we understand why we do it: speech precedes grammar, reason precedes logic; and so a division of animals into groups, upon an instinctive perception of their differences, has preceded all our scientific creeds and doctrines. Let us, therefore, proceed to examine the meaning of these names as adopted by naturalists.

When Cuvier proposed his four primary divisions of the animal kingdom, he added his argument for their adoption— *because*, he said, they are constructed on four different plans. All the progress in our science since his time confirms this result; and I shall attempt to show that there are really four, and only four, such structional ideas at the foundation of the animal kingdom, and that all animals are included under one or another of them. But it does not follow, that, because we have arrived at a sound principle, we are therefore unerring in our practice. From ignorance we may misplace animals, and include them under the wrong division. This is a mistake, however, which a better insight into their organization rectifies; and experience constantly proves, that, whenever the structure of an animal is perfectly under-stood, there is no hesitation as to the head under which it be-longs. We may consequently test the merits of these four primary groups on the evidence furnished by investigation.

It has already been seen that these plans may be presented in the most abstract manner without any reference to special animals. *Radiation* expresses in one word the idea on which the lowest of these types is based. In *Radiates* we have no promi-nent bilateral symmetry, such as exists in all other animals, but an all-sided symmetry, in which there is no right and left, no an-terior and posterior extremity, no above and below. It is true that in some of them there are indications of that bilateral symmetry which becomes a law in the higher animals; but wherever such a tendency is perceptible in the Radiates it is subordinate to the typical plan on which the whole group is founded. They are spheroidal bodies; yet, though many of them remind us of a sphere, they are by no means to be compared to a mathematical sphere, but rather to an organic sphere, so loaded with life, as it were, as to produce an infinite variety of radiate symmetry. The mathematical sphere has a centre to which every point of the surface bears identical relations; such spheres do not exist in the Animal Kingdom. A sphere of revolution, in consequence of its rotation up on its axis, presents equally flattened poles with me-ridians of equal value; this also is no organic character. A living sphere has unequal poles as well as unequal meridians, however much it may resemble a perfectly spheroidal body, and the whole organization is arranged, not necessarily around a centre, but always around a vertical axis, to which the parts bear equal relations.

In *Mollusks* there is a longitudinal axis and a bilateral sym-metry; but the longitudinal axis in these soft concentrated bodies is not very prominent, except in the highest class; and though the two ends of this axis are distinct from each other, the difference is not so marked that we can say at once, for all of them, which is the anterior and which the posterior extremity. In this type, right and left have the preponderance over the other diameters of the body. The sides are the prominent parts—they are loaded with the most important organs, or with those peculiarities of the structure that give it character. The Oyster is a good instance of this, with its double valve, so swollen on one side, so flat on the other. There is an unconscious recognition of this in the arrangement of all collections of Mollusks; for, though the collectors do not put up their specimens with any intention of illustrating this peculiarity, they instinctively give them the position best calculated to display their distinctive characteristics, and to accomplish this they necessarily place them in such a manner as to show the sides.

In *Articulates* there is also a longitudinal axis of the body and a bilateral symmetry in the arrangement of parts; the head and tail are marked, and the right and left sides are distinct. But the prominent tendency in this type is the development of the dorsal and ventral region; here above and below prevail over right and left. It is the back and lower side that have the preponderance over any other part of the structure in Articulates. The body is divided from end to end by a succession of transverse constrictions, forming movable rings; but the striking features of the animal are always above or below, and especially developed on the back. Any collection of Insects or Crustacea is an evidence of this; being always instinctively arranged in such a manner as to show the predominant features, they uniformly exhibit the back of the animal. The profile view of an Articulate has no significance; whereas in a Mollusk, on the contrary, the profile view is the most illustrative of the structural character.

In the highest division, the *Vertebrates,* so characteristically called by Baer the *Doubly Symmetrical* type, a solid column runs through the body with an arch above and an arch below, thus forming a double internal cavity. In this type, the head is the prominent feature; it is, as it were, the loaded end of the longitudinal axis, so charged with vitality as to form an intelligent brain, and rising in man to such predominance as to command and control the whole organism. The structure is arranged above and below this axis, the upper cavity containing, as we have seen above, all the sensitive organs, and the lower cavity containing all those by which life is maintained.

While Cuvier and his followers traced these four distinct plans, as shown in the adult animal, Baer opened to us a new

field of investigation in the embryology of the four types, showing that for each there was a special mode of growth in the egg.
Looking at them from this point of view, we shall see that these
four types, with their four modes of growth, seem to fill out completely the plan or outline of the animal kingdom, and leave no
reason to expect any further development or any other plan of
animal life within these limits. The eggs of all animals are
spheres, such as I have described them; but in the Radiate the
whole periphery is transformed into the germ, so that it becomes, by the liquefying of the yolk, a hollow sphere. In the
Mollusks, the germ lies above the yolk, absorbing its whole substance through the underside, thus forming a massive close body
instead of a hollow one. In the Articulate, the germ is turned in a
position exactly opposite to that of the Mollusk, and absorbs the
yolk upon the back. In the Vertebrate, the germ divides in two
folds, one turning upward, the other turning downward, above
and below the central backbone. These four modes of development seem to exhaust the possibilities of the primitive sphere,
which is the foundation of all animal life, and therefore I believe
that Cuvier and Baer were right in saying that the whole animal
kingdom is included under these four structural ideas.

Leuckart proposed to subdivide the Radiates into two
groups: the Coelenterata, including Polyps and Acalephs or
Jelly-Fishes—and Echinoderms, including Star-Fishes, Sea-Urchins, and Holothurians. His reason for this distinction is the
fact, that in the latter the organs or cavities of the body have
walls of their own, distinct from the body-wall; whereas in the
former they are formed by internal folds of the outer wall of the
body, as in the Polyps, or are hollowed out of the substance of
the body, as in Jelly-Fishes. This implies no difference in the
plan, but merely a difference in the execution of the plan. Both
are equally radiate in their structure; and when Leuckart separated them as distinct primary types, he mistook a difference in
the material expression of the plan for a difference in the plan itself.

So some naturalists have distinguished Worms from the
other Articulates as a separate prime division. But the structural
plan of this type is a cylinder divided by transverse constrictions

or joints; and whether those joints are uniformly arranged from one end of the body to the other, as in the Worms, or whether the front joints are soldered together so as to form two regions of the body, as in Crustacea, or divided so as to form three regions of the body, as in winged insects, does not in the least affect the typical character of the structure, which remains the same in all, being, in fact, an articulated cylinder with variously combined rings and more or less complicated tubular appendages.

Branches or types, then, are natural groups of the animal kingdom, founded on plans of structure or structural ideas. What now are classes? Are they lesser divisions, differing only in extent, or are they founded on special characters? I believe the latter view to be the true one, and that class characters have a significance quite different from that of their mere range or extent. These divisions are founded on certain categories of structure; and were there but one animal of a class in the world, if it had those characters on which a class is founded, it would be as distinct from all other classes as if its kind were counted by thousands.

Baer approached the idea of the classes when he discriminated between plan of structure or type and the degree of perfection in the structure. But while he understands the distinction between a plan and its execution, his ideas respecting the different features of structure are not quite so precise. He does not, for instance, distinguish between the complication of a given structure and the mode of execution of a plan, both of which are combined in what he calls degrees of perfection. And yet, without this distinction, the difference between classes and orders cannot be understood; for classes and orders rest upon a just appreciation of these two categories, which are quite distinct from each other, and have by no means the same significance.

Again, quite distinct from both of these is the character of form, not to be confounded either with complication of structure, on which orders are based, or with the execution of the plan, on which classes rest. An example will show that form is no guide for the determination of classes or orders. Take, for instance, a Beche-de-Mer, a member of the highest class of Radiates, and compare it with a Worm. They are both long cylindrical bodies; but one has parallel divisions along the length of the body; the other has the body divided by transverse rings. Though in external form they resemble each other, the one is a worm-like Radiate, the other is a worm-like Articulate, each having the structure of its own type; so that they do not even belong to the same great division of the animal kingdom, much less to the same class. We have a similar instance in the Whales and Fishes—the Whales having been for a long time considered as Fishes, on account of their form, while their structural complication shows them to be a low order of the class of Mammalia, to which we ourselves belong, that class being founded upon a particular mode of execution of the plan characteristic of the Vertebrates, while the order to which the Whales belong depends upon their complication of structure, as compared with other members of the same class.

We may therefore say that neither form nor complication of structure distinguishes classes, but simply the mode of execution of a plan. In Vertebrates, for instance, how do we distinguish the class of Mammalia from the other classes of the type? By the peculiar development of the brain, by their breathing through lungs, by their double circulation, by their bringing forth living young and nursing them with milk. In this class the beasts of prey form a distinct order, superior to the Whales or the herbivorous animals, on account of the higher complication of their structure; and for the same reason we place the Monkeys above them all. But among the beasts of prey we distinguish the Bears, as a family, from the family of Dogs, Wolves, and Cats, on account of their different form, which does not imply a difference either in the complication of their structure or in the mode of execution of their plan.

V.

Evolution and Permanence of Type

Note

"Evolution and Permanence of Type," published a few months after Agassiz's death, is a magazine article setting forth his final statement about Darwinian theory and the nature of reality. This single document marks the end of a tradition of thought that began with Aristotle. The system it posited, like that of physics in the same century, was closed and of known limits. The scholars had set out to chart the intricacy of the design. With the discovery of radioactivity and of evolution, a new cycle of knowledge began, and Agassiz's world was shut off from our own as sharply as if it had been frozen like a mammoth in a glacier. And like the mammoth it was frozen intact, whole, inspectable. The strength and penetration of Agassiz's mind are reflected in this ultimate statement, a concentration of last force.

V. Evolution and Permanence of Type

In connection with modern views of science we hear so much of evolution and evolutionists that it is worth our while to ask if there is any such process as evolution in nature. Unquestionably, yes. But all that is actually known of this process we owe to the great embryologists of our century, Döllinger and his pupils K. E. von Baer, Pander, and others—the men in short who have founded the science of Embryology. It is true there are younger men who have done since, and are doing now, noble work in this field of research; but the glory must, after all, be given to those who opened the way in which more recent students are pressing forward.

The pioneers in the science of Embryology, by a series of investigations which will challenge admiration as long as patience and accuracy of research are valued, have proved that all living beings produce eggs, and that these eggs contain a yolk-substance out of which new beings, identical with their parents, are evolved by a succession of gradual changes. These successive stages of growth constitute evolution, as understood by embryologists, and within these limits all naturalists who know anything of Zoology may be said to be evolutionists. The law of evolution, however, so far as its working is understood, is a law controlling development and keeping types within appointed cycles of growth, which revolve forever upon themselves, returning at appointed intervals to the same starting-point and repeating through a succession of phases the same course. These cycles have never been known to oscillate or to pass into each other; indeed, the only structural differences known between individuals of the same stock are monstrosities or peculiarities pertaining to sex, and the latter are as abiding and permanent as to type itself. Taken together the relations of sex constitute one of the most obscure and wonderful features of the whole organic world, all the more impressive for its universality.

Under the recent and novel application of the terms "evolution" and "evolutionist," we are in danger of forgetting the only process of the kind in the growth of animals which has actually been demonstrated, as well as the men to whom we owe that demonstration. Indeed, the science of Zoology, including everything pertaining to the past and present life and history of animals, has furnished, since the beginning of the nineteenth century, an amount of startling and exciting information in which men have lost sight of the old landmarks. In the present ferment of theories respecting the relations of animals to one another, their origin, growth, and diversity, those broader principles of our science—upon which the whole animal kingdom has been divided into a few grand comprehensive types, each one a structural unit in itself—are completely overlooked.

It is not very long since, with the exception of Insects, all the lower animals were grouped together in one division as Worms, on account of their simple structure. A century ago this classification, established by Linnaeus, was still unquestioned. Cuvier was the first to introduce a classification based not merely upon a more or less complicated organization but upon ideas or plans of structure. He recognized four of these plans in the whole animal kingdom, neither more nor less. However, when this principle was first announced, the incompleteness of our knowledge made it impossible to apply it correctly in every case, and Cuvier himself placed certain animals of obscure or intricate structure under the wrong head. Nevertheless the law was sanctioned, and gave at once a new aim and impulse to investigation. This idea of structural plans, as the foundation of a natural classification, dates only from the year 1812, and was first presented by Cuvier in the Annals of the Museum in Paris.

About the same time another great investigator, Karl Ernst von Baer, then a young naturalist, Döllinger's favorite and most original pupil, was studying in Germany the growth of the chicken in the egg. In a different branch of research, though bearing equally on the structural relations of organized beings, he, without knowing of Cuvier's investigations, arrived at a like conclusion, namely, that there are four different modes of growth among animals. This result has only been confirmed by later investigators. Every living creature is formed in an egg and grows

up according to a pattern and a mode of development common
to its type, and of these embryonic norms there are but four.
Here, then, was a double confirmation of the distinct circumscription of types, as based upon structure, announced almost simultaneously by two independent investigators, ignorant of each
other's work, and arriving at the same result by different methods. The one, building up from the first dawn of life in the embryonic germs of various animals, worked out the four great
types of organic life from the beginning; while his co-worker
reached the same end through a study of their perfected structure
in adult forms. Starting from diametrically opposite points, they
met at last on the higher ground to which they were both led by
their respective studies.

For a quarter of a century following, the aim of all naturalists was to determine the relations of these groups to one another
with greater precision, and to trace the affinities between the
minor divisions of the whole animal kingdom. It was natural to
suppose that all living beings were in some way or other connected; and, indeed, the discoveries in Geology, with its buried
remains of extinct life, following fast upon those of Cuvier in
structure and of Von Baer in Embryology, seemed to reveal,
however dimly and in broken outlines, a consistent history carried on coherently through all times and extending gradually
over the whole surface of the earth, until it culminated in the
animal kingdom as it at present exists, with man at its head.

The next step, though a natural result of the flood of facts
poured in upon us under the new stimulus to research, led men
away from the simple and, as I believe, sound principles of classification established by the two great masters of zoological
science. The announcement of four typical divisions in the animal kingdom stirred investigators to a closer comparison of their
structure. The science of Comparative Anatomy made rapid
strides; and since the ability of combining facts is a much rarer
gift than that of discerning them, many students lost sight of the
unity of structural design in the multiplicity of structural detail.
The natural result of this was a breaking up of the four great
groups of Radiates, Mollusks, Articulates and Vertebrates into a
larger number of primary divisions. Classifications were multi-

plied with astonishing rapidity, and each writer had his own system of nomenclature, until our science was perplexingly burdened with synonyms. I may mention, as a sample, one or two of the more prominent changes introduced at this time into the general classification of animals.

The Radiates had been divided by Cuvier into three classes, to which, on imperfect data, he erroneously added the Intestinal Worms and the Infusoria. These classes, as they now stand according to his classification, with some recent improvements, are Polyps (corals, sea-anemones, and the like), Acalephs (jelly-fishes), and Echinoderms (star-fishes, sea-urchins, and holothurians, better known, perhaps, as Beche-de-mer). Of these three classes the two first, Polyps and Acalephs, were set apart by Leuckart and other naturalists as "Coelenterata," while the Echinoderms by themselves were elevated into a primary division. There is, however, no valid ground for this. The plan of structure is the same in all three classes, the only difference being that various organs which in the Polyps and the Acalephs are, as it were, simply hollowed out of the substance of the body, have in the Echinoderms walls of their own. This is a special complication of structural execution, but makes no difference in the structural plan. The organs and the whole structural combination are the same in the two divisions. In the same way Cephalopods, squids and the cuttlefishes, which form the highest class among Mollusks, were separated from the Gasteropods and Acephala, and set apart as a distinct type, because their eggs undergo only a surface segmentation instead of being segmented through and through, as is the case with the members of the two other classes. But this surface segmentation leads ultimately to a structure which has the same essential features as that of the other Mollusks. Indeed, we find also in other branches of the animal kingdom, the Vertebrates for instance, partial or total segmentation, in different classes; but it does not lead to any typical differences there, any more than among Mollusks. Another instance is that of the Bryozoa and Tunicata, which were separated from the Mollusks on account of the greater simplicity of their structure and associated with those simpler Worms in which articulated limbs are wanting. In short, the numerous types admitted nowadays by most zoologists are founded only upon structural complication, without special regard to the plan of their structure; and the comprehensive principle of structural conception or plan, as determining the primary types, so impressive when first announced, has gradually lost its hold upon naturalists through their very familiarity with special complications of structure. But since we are still in doubt as to the true nature of many organisms, such as the sponges and the Protozoa so-called, it is too early to affirm positively that all the primary divisions of the animal kingdom are included in Cuvier's four types. Yet it is safe to say that no primary division will stand which does not bear the test he applied to the four great groups, Radiates, Mollusks, Articulates, and Vertebrates, namely, that of a distinct plan of structure for each.

The time has, perhaps, not come for an impartial appreciation of the views of Darwin, and the task is the more difficult because it involves an equally impartial review of the modifications his theory has undergone at the hands of his followers. The aim of his first work on The Origin of Species was to show that neither vegetable nor animal forms are so distinct from one another or so independent in their origin and structural relations as most naturalists believed. This idea was not new. Under different aspects it had been urged repeatedly for more than a century by DeMaillet, by Lamarck, by E. Geoffroy St. Hilaire and others; nor was it wholly original even with them, for the study of the relations of animals and plants has at all times been one of the principal aims of all the more advanced students of Natural History; they have differed only in their methods and appreciations. But Darwin has placed the subject on a different basis from that of all his predecessors, and has brought to the discussion a vast amount of well-arranged information, a convincing cogency of argument, and a captivating charm of presentation. His doctrine appealed the more powerfully to the scientific world because he maintained it at first not upon metaphysical ground but upon observation. Indeed it might be said that he treated his subject according to the best scientific methods, had he not frequently overstepped the boundaries of actual knowledge and allowed his imagination to supply the links which science does not furnish.

The excitement produced by the publication of The Origin of Species may be fairly compared to that which followed the appearance of Oken's Natur-Philosphie, over fifty years ago, in which it was claimed that the key had been found to the whole system of organic life. According to Oken, the animal kingdom, in all its diversity, is but the presentation in detail of the organization of man. The Infusoria are the primordial material of life scattered broadcast everywhere, and man himself but a complex of such Infusoria. The Vertebrates represent what Oken calls flesh, that is, bones, muscles, nerves, and the senses, in various combinations; the Fishes are Bone-animals (Knochen-Thiere); the Reptiles, Muscle-animals (Muskel-Thiere); the Birds, Nerve-animals (Nerven-Thiere); the Mammals—with man, combining in his higher structure the whole scheme of organic life, at their head—are Sense-animals (Sinnen-Thiere). The parallelism was drawn with admirable skill and carried into the secondary divisions, down to the families and even the genera. The Articulates were likened to the systems of respiration and circulation; the Mollusks to those of reproduction; the Radiates to those of digestion. The comprehensiveness and grandeur of these views, in which the scattered elements of organic life, serving distinct purposes in the lower animals, are gathered into one structural combination in the highest living being appealed powerfully to the imagination. In Germany they were welcomed with an enthusiasm such as is shown there for Darwinism. England was lukewarm, and France turned a cold shoulder, as she at present does to the theory of the great English naturalist. The influence of Cuvier and the Jussieux was deeply felt in Western Europe, and perhaps saved French naturalists from falling into a fanciful but attractive doctrine, numbered now among the exploded theories of the past.

Darwin's first work, though it did not immediately meet with the universal acceptance since accorded to it, excited, nevertheless, intense and general interest. The circumstance that almost identical views were simultaneously expressed by Wallace, and that several prominent investigators hailed them as the solution of the great problem, gave them double strength; for it seemed improbable that so many able students of nature should agree in their interpretation of facts, unless that interpretation were the true one. The Origin of Species was followed by a second work, The Variation of Animals and Plants under Domestication, to which a third soon succeeded, The Descent of Man. The last phase of the doctrine is its identification with metaphysics in Darwin's latest work on The Expression of the Emotions in Man and Animals. I can only rejoice that the discussion has taken this turn, much as I dissent from the treatment of the subject. It cannot be too soon understood that science is one, and that whether we investigate language, philosophy, theology, history, or physics, we are dealing with the same problem, culminating in the knowledge of ourselves. Speech is known only in connection with the organs of man, thought in connection with his brain, religion as the expression of his aspirations, history as the record of his deeds, and physical sciences as the laws under which he lives. Philosophers and theologians have yet to learn that a physical fact is as sacred as a moral principle. Our own nature demands from us this double allegiance.

It is hardly necessary to give here an analysis of the theory contained in these works of Darwin. Its watchwords, "natural selection," "struggle for existence," "survival of the fittest," are equally familiar to those who do and to those who do not understand them; as well known, indeed, to the amateur in science as to the professional naturalist. It is supported by a startling array of facts respecting the changes animals undergo under domestication, respecting the formation of breeds and varieties, respecting metamorphoses, respecting the dangers to life among all animals and the way in which nature meets them, respecting the influence of climate and external conditions upon superficial structural features, and respecting natural preferences and proclivities between animals as influencing the final results of interbreeding. In the Variation of Animals and Plants under Domestication all that experiments in breeding or fancy horticulture could teach, whether as recorded in the literature and traditions of the subject or gathered from the practical farmers, stock-breeders, and gardeners, was brought together and presented with equal erudition and clearness. No fact was omitted showing the pliability of plants and animals under the fostering care of man. The final conclusion of the author is summed up in his theory of Pangenesis. And yet this book does but prove more conclusively what was already known, namely, that all domesticated animals and cultivated plants are traceable to distinct species, and that the domesticated pigeons which furnish so large a portion of the illustration are, notwithstanding their great diversity under special treatment, no exception to this rule. The truth is, our domesticated animals, with all their breeds and varieties, have never been traced back to anything but their own species, nor have artificial varieties, so far as we know, failed to revert to the wild stock when left to themselves. Darwin's works and those of his followers have added nothing new to our previous knowledge concerning the origin of man and his associates in domestic life, the horse, the cow, the sheep, the dog, or, indeed, of any animal. The facts upon which Darwin, Wallace, Haeckel, and others base their views are in the possession of every well-educated naturalist. It is only a question of interpretation, not of discovery or of new and unlooked-for information.

Darwin's third book, The Descent of Man, treats a more difficult part of the subject. In this book the question of genealogy is the prominent topic. It had been treated already, it is true, in The Origin of Species, but with no special allusion to mankind. The structure was as yet a torso, a trunk without a head. In these two volumes the whole ground of heredity, of qualities transmitted to the new individual by his progenitors, and that of resemblance—whether physical, intellectual, or moral, between mankind and the higher mammalia, and especially between ourselves and our nearest relations, the anthropoid monkeys—are brought out with the fullness of material and the skill of treatment so characteristic of the author. But here again the reader seeks in vain for any evidence of a transition between man and his fellow-creatures. Indeed, both with Darwin and his followers, a great part of the argument is purely negative. It rests partly upon the assumption that, in the succession of ages, just those transition types have dropped out from the geological record which would have proved the Darwinian conclusions had these types been preserved, and that in the living animal the process of transition is too subtle for detection. Darwin and his followers thus throw off the responsibility of proof with respect both to embryonic growth and geological succession.

Within the last three or four years, however, it has seemed as if new light were about to be thrown at least upon one of these problems. Two prominent naturalists announced that they had found indications of a direct structural connection between primary types: in the one case between Mollusks and Vertebrates, in the other between Radiates and Articulates. The first of these views was published by a Russian investigator of great skill and eminence, Kowalevsky. He stated that the Ascidians (the so-called soft-shelled clams) showed, in the course of their growth, a string of cells corresponding to the dorsal cord in Vertebrates. For the uninitiated I must explain that, at one stage of its development, in the upper layer of cells of which the Vertebrate germ consists, there arise two folds which, curving upward and inward, form first a longitudinal furrow and finally a cavity for the nervous centres, the brain and spinal cord, while the lower layer of these cells folds downward to enclose the organs of digestion, circulation, and reproduction. Between these two folds, but on the dorsal side, that is, along the back, under the spinal marrow, arises a solid string of more condensed substance, which develops into the dorsal cord, the basis of the backbone. Kowalevsky describes, in the Ascidians, a formation of longitudinally arranged cells as representing an incipient backbone, running from the middle of the body into the tail, along a furrow of the germ of these animals in which the main nervous swelling is situated. This was hailed as a great discovery by the friends of the transmutation theory. At last the transition point was found between the lower and higher animals, and man himself was traced back to the Ascidians. One could hardly open a scientific journal or any popular essay on Natural History, without meeting some allusion to the Ascidians as our ancestors. Not only was it seized upon by the many amateur contributors to the literature of this subject, but Darwin himself, and his ardent followers, welcomed this first direct evidence of structural affinity between the Vertebrates and the lower animals.

The existence of these cells, though never thought of in this light before, was not unknown to naturalists. I have myself seen and examined them, and had intended to say something in this article of their nature and position; but while I was preparing it for the press the subject was taken from me and treated by the hand of a master whom all naturalists venerate. I have received very recently from the aged Nestor of the science of Embryology, K. E. von Baer, to whose early investigations I have already alluded, a pamphlet upon the development of the Ascidians as compared to that of the Vertebrates. There is something touching in the conditions under which he enters the lists with the younger men who have set aside the great laws of typical structure, to the interpretation of which his whole life has been given. He is now very feeble and nearly blind; but the keen, far-reaching, internal sight is undimmed by age. With the precision and ease which only a complete familiarity with all the facts can give, he shows that the actual development of the Ascidians has no true homology with that of the Vertebrates; that the string of cells in the former—compared to the dorsal cord of the latter—does not run along the back at all, but is placed on the ventral side of the body. To say that the first Vertebrates or their progenitors carried their backbones in this fashion is about as reasonable as to say that they walked on their heads. It is reversing their whole structure, and putting their vertebral column where the abdominal cavity should be. Von Baer closes his paper in these words: "It will readily be granted that I have written for zoologists and anatomists; but I may perhaps be blamed for being frequently very circumstantial where a brief allusion would have been sufficient. In so doing, I had the many dilletanti in view, who believe in complete transmutations, and who might be disposed to consider it mere conceit not to recognize the Ascidians as the ancestors of Man. I beg to apologize for some repetitions arising from this consideration for the dilletanti."

The other so-called discovery is that of Haeckel, that starfishes are compound animals, made up, as it were, of worm-like beings united like rays in one organism. A similar opinion had already been entertained by Duvernoy, and in a measure also by Oken, who described the Echinoderms as Radiate-worms. This doctrine, if true, would at once establish a transition from Radiates to Articulates. There is, in the first place, not the slightest foundation for this assumption in the structure of star-fish. The arms of these animals are made up of the same parts as the vertical zones of a sea-urchin and of all the Radiates, and have no resemblance whatever to the structure of the Worms. Each ambulacral zone of a star-fish or a sea-urchin is strictly homological to a structural segment of an Acaleph or to a radiating chamber of a Polyp. Moreover, the homology between a sea-urchin and a star-fish is complete; if one is an organic unit the other must be also, and no one ever suggested that the sea-urchin was anything but a single organism. In comparing the Radiates with other animals, it is essential to place them in the same attitude, so that we compare like with like; otherwise, we make the mistake of the Russian naturalist, and compare the front side of one animal with the dorsal side of another, or the upper side of one with the lower side of another; thus taking mere superficial resemblance between totally distinct parts for true homologies. In all Mollusks, Articulates, and Vertebrates the parts are arranged along a longitudinal axis; in Radiates alone they are disposed around a vertical axis, like spherical wedges, comparable in some instances to the segments of an orange. This organic formula, for so we may call it, is differently expressed and more or less distinct in different Radiates. It may be built up in a sphere, as in the sea-urchins, or opened out into a star, like the five-finger; it may be in the form of a sac divided internally, as in the sea-anemones, or in that of a disk, channelled or furrowed so as to divide it into equal segments, like the jelly-fish; but upon comparison the same structural elements are found in all. These structural elements bear an identical relation to the vertical axis of the animals. To compare any Radiate with any Articulate is therefore to compare the vertical axis of one animal with the horizontal axis of the other. The parallelism will not bear examination any more than that between the Mollusks and Vertebrates. Even in those holothurians and sea-urchins in which one side of the body is flattened, the structure exhibits the same plan and the parts are arranged in the same way as in all other Radiates, whatever be their natural attitude in the element in which they live; whether they stand upright with the mouth turned upward, or hang down in the reverse position, or crawl about horizontally. In like manner the vertical position of man in no way invalidates the homology of his organization with that of the fishes, reptiles, birds, and mammalia. These two cases are thus far the only instances which have been brought forward to prove actual structural affinity between distinct primary divisions of the animal kingdom.

It is not my intention to take up categorically all the different points on which the modern theory of transmutation is based. Metamorphosis plays a large part in it, and is treated as an evidence of transition from one animal into another. The truth is that metamorphosis, like all embryonic growth, is a normal process of development, moving in regular cycles, returning always to the same starting-point, and leading always to the same end; such are the alternate generations in the lower animals and the metamorphoses in higher ones, as in the butterflies and other insects, or in certain reptiles, frogs and toads, salamanders, and the like. In some of these types the development lasts for a long time and the stages of embryonic growth are often so distinct that, until the connection between them is traced, each phase may seem like a separate existence, whereas they are only chapters in one and the same life. I have myself watched carefully all the successive changes of development in the North American Axolotl, whose recently discovered metamorphoses have led to much discussion in connection with the modern doctrine of evolution. I can see no difference between this and other instances of metamorphosis. Certain organs, conspicuous in one phase of the animal's life, are resorbed and disappear in a succeeding phase. But this does not differ at all from like processes in the toads and frogs, for instance; nor does it even differ essentially from like processes in the ordinary growth of all animals. The higher Vertebrates, including man himself, breathe through gill-like organs in the early part of their life. These gills disappear and give place to lungs only in a later phase of their existence. Metamorphoses have all the constancy and invariability of other modes of embryonic growth, and have never been known to lead to any transition of one species into another.

Another fertile topic in connection with this theory is that of heredity. No one can deny that inheritance is a powerful factor in the maintenance of race and in the improvement of breeds and varieties. But it has never been known that acquired qualities, even though retained through successive generations, have led to the production of new species. Darwin's attractive style is never more alluring than in connection with this subject. His concise and effective phrases have the weight of aphorisms and pass current for principles, when they may be only unfounded assertions. Such is "the survival of the fittest." After reading some chapters of The Descent of Man, could any one doubt, unless indeed he happened to be familiar with the facts, that animals, possessing certain advantages over others, are necessarily winners in the race for life? And yet it is not true that, outside of the influence of man, there are, in nature, privileged individuals among animals capable of holding on to a positive gain, generation after generation, and of transmitting successfully their peculiarities until they become the starting point for another step; the descendants losing at last, through this cumulative process, all close resemblance to their progenitors. It is not true that a slight variation, among the successive offspring of the same stock, goes on increasing until the difference amounts to a specific distinction. On the contrary, it is a matter of fact that extreme variations finally degenerate or become sterile; like monstrosities they die out, or return to their type.

The whole subject of inheritance is exceedingly intricate, working often in a seemingly capricious and fitful way. Qualities, both good and bad, are dropped as well as acquired, and the process ends sometimes in the degradation of the type and the survival of the unfit rather than the fittest. The most trifling and fantastic tricks of inheritance are quoted in support of the transmutation theory; but little is said of the sudden apparition of powerful original qualities which almost always rise like pure creations and are gone with their day and generation. The noblest gifts are exceptional, and are rarely inherited; this very fact seems to me an evidence of something more and higher than mere evolution and transmission concerned in the problem of life.

In the same way, the matter of natural and sexual selection is susceptible of very various interpretations. No doubt, on the whole, Nature protects her best. But it would not be difficult to bring together an array of facts as striking as those produced by the evolutionists in favor of their theory, to show that sexual selection is by no means always favorable to the elimination of the chaff and the preservation of the wheat. A natural attraction, independent of strength or beauty, is an unquestionable element in this problem, and its action is seen among animals as well as among men. The fact that fine progeny are not infrequently the offspring of weak parents and *vice versa* points perhaps to some innate power of redress by which the caprices of choice are counterbalanced. But there can be no doubt that types are as often endangered as protected by the so-called law of sexual selection.

As to the influence of climate and physical conditions, we all know their power for evil and for good upon living beings. But there is, nevertheless, nothing more striking in the whole book of nature than the power shown by types and species to resist physical conditions. Endless evidence may be brought from the whole expanse of land and air and water, showing that identical physical conditions will do nothing toward the merging of species into one another, neither will variety of conditions do anything toward their multiplication. One thing only we know absolutely, and in this treacherous, marshy ground of hypothesis and assumption, it is pleasant to plant one's foot occasionally upon a solid fact here and there. Whatever be the means of preserving and transmitting properties, the primitive types have remained permanent and unchanged—in the long succession of ages amid all the appearance and disappearance of kinds, the fading away of one species and the coming in of another—from the earliest geological periods to the present day. How these types were first introduced, how the species which have successively represented them have replaced one another—these are the vital questions to which no answer has been given. We are as far from any satisfactory solution of this problem as if development theories had never been discussed.

This brings us to the geological side of the question. As a

palaeontologist I have from the beginning stood aloof from this
new theory of transmutation, now so widely admitted by the
scientific world. Its doctrines, in fact, contradict what the animal
forms buried in the rocky strata of our earth tell us of their own
introduction and succession upon the surface of the globe. Let us
therefore hear them;—for, after all, their testimony is that of the
eye-witness and the actor in the scene. Take first the type to
which we ourselves belong. If it be true that there has been a
progressive transmutation of the whole type of Vertebrates, beginning with the lowest and culminating in the highest, the earlier should of course be structurally inferior to the later ones.
What then is the lowest* living Vertebrate? Every zoologist will
answer, The Amphioxus, that elongated, worm-like Vertebrate
whose organization is nothing more than a dorsal cord, with a
nervous thread above, and a respiratory and digestive cavity below, containing also the reproductive organs, the whole being
clothed in flesh. Yet low as it is in the scale of life, the Amphioxus
is, by virtue of its vertebral column, a member of the same type
as ourselves. Next to the Amphioxus come the Myxinoids, structurally but little above them, and the Lamper-eels. These are the
animals which Haeckel places at the base of his zoological tree,
rooting the whole Vertebrate branch of the animal kingdom in
the Amphioxus as the forefather (Stamm-Vater) of the type. Let
us look now at the earliest Vertebrates, as known and recorded in
geological surveys. They should of course, if there is any truth in
the transmutation theory, correspond with the lowest in rank or
standing. What then are the earliest known Vertebrates? They are
Selachians (sharks and their allies) and Ganoids (garpikes and
the like), the highest of all living fishes, structurally speaking. I
shall be answered that these belong to the Silurian and Devonian
periods, and that it is believed that Vertebrates may have existed
before that time. It will also be argued that Myzonts, namely
Amphioxus, Myxinoids, and Lamper-eels, have no hard parts and
could not have been preserved on that account. I will grant both
these points, though the fact is that the Myzonts do possess solid

---

* I use the terms low and high, throughout, in the zoological sense;
with reference to specialization of structure, as comparative anatomists
understand it.

parts, in the jaws, as capable of preservation as any bone, and that these solid parts, if ever found, even singly, would be as significant, for a zoologist, as the whole skeleton. Granting also that Amphioxus-like fishes may have lived and may have disappeared before the Silurian period; the Silurian deposits follow immediately upon those in which life first appeared, and should therefore contain not the highest fishes, but the fishes next in order to the Myzonts, and these are certainly neither the Ganoids nor the Selachians. The presence of the Selachians at the dawn of life upon earth is in direct contradiction to the idea of a gradual progressive development. They are nevertheless exceedingly abundant in the Palaeozoic beds, and these fossil forms are so similar to the living representatives of the same group that what is true of the organization and development of the latter is unquestionably equally true of the former. In all their features the Selachians, more than any other fishes, resemble the higher animals. They lay few eggs, the higher kinds giving birth only to three, four, or five at a brood, whereas the common fishes lay myriads of eggs, hundreds of thousands in some instances, and these are for the greater part cast into the water to be developed at random. The limitation of the young is unquestionably a mark of superiority. The higher we rise in the scale of animal life the more restricted is the number of offspring. In proportion to this reduction in number, the connection of the offspring with the parent is drawn closer, organically and morally, till this relation becomes finally the foundation of all social organization, of all human civilization. In some Selachians there is an actual organic connection between parent and progeny, resembling the placental connection which marks the embryonic development of the higher Vertebrates. This feature is in harmony with the sexual relations among them; for it is of all facts in their organic history the most curious, that, among Vertebrates, the Selachians are the only ones with whom the connection of sexes recalls that of the human family. Now, these higher fishes being the first representatives of the Vertebrates on earth, or at least those next following their earliest representatives, where do we find the Myzonts, fishes which are structurally inferior to all others, and of which the Amphioxus is the lowest member? They come in during the latest period of our world's history, with what is called the present period, to which we ourselves belong. This certainly does not look like a connected series beginning with the lowest and ending with the highest, for the highest fishes come first and the lowest come last.

The companions of the Selachians in the earlier geological periods, the Ganoids, belong also to the higher representatives of the class of fishes. Some of them have the ball-and-socket vertebral joint of the reptiles and birds, enabling the head to move upon the neck with greater freedom than in the lower fishes. I am aware that these synthetic and prophetic types, which I have myself been the first to point out, and in which features of higher and later groups are combined or hinted at in lower and earlier ones, have been interpreted as transition types. It has even been said that I have myself furnished the strongest evidence of the transmutation theory. This might perhaps be so, did these types follow, instead of preceding, the lower fishes. But the whole history of geological succession shows us that the lowest in structure is by no means necessarily the earliest in time, either in the Vertebrate type or any other. Synthetic and prophetic types have accompanied the introduction of all the primary divisions of the animal kingdom. With these may be found what I have called embryonic types, which never rise, even in their adult state, above those conditions which in higher structures are but the prelude to the adult state. It may, therefore, truly be said that a great diversity of types has existed from the beginning.

The most advanced Darwinians seem reluctant to acknowledge the intervention of an intellectual power in the diversity which obtains in nature, under the plea that such an admission implies distinct creative acts for every species. What of it, if it were true? Have those who object to repeated acts of creation ever considered that no progress can be made in knowledge without repeated acts of thinking? And what are thoughts but specific acts of the mind? Why should it then be unscientific to infer that the facts of nature are the result of a similar process, since there is no evidence of any other cause? The world has arisen in some way or other. How it originated is the great question, and Darwin's theory, like all other attempts to explain the origin of life, is thus far merely conjectural. I believe he has not even made the best conjecture possible in the present state of our knowledge.

The more I look at the great complex of the animal world, the more sure do I feel that we have not yet reached its hidden meaning, and the more do I regret that the young and ardent spirits of our day give themselves to speculation rather than to close and accurate investigation.

I hope in future articles to show, first, that, however broken the geological record may be, there is a complete sequence in many parts of it, from which the character of the succession may be ascertained; secondly, that, since the most exquisitely delicate structures, as well as embryonic phases of growth of the most perishable nature, have been preserved from the very early deposits, we have no right to infer the disappearance of types because their absence disproves some favorite theory; and, lastly, that there is no evidence of a direct descent of later from earlier species in the geological succession of animals.

Chronology

1807 Jean Louis Rodolphe Agassiz born May 28, the son of Pastor Rodolphe and Rose Mayor Agassiz, at Motier, Switzerland.

1817 Entered the Collège de Bienne, a school for boys twenty miles from Motier, having been taught until this time by his father at home. His courses at Bienne were Greek, Latin, Mathematics, German and Italian.

1822 Entered the Academy at Lausanne.

1824 Entered the Medical School at Zurich.

1826 Entered Heidelberg.

1827 Entered the University of Munich.

1828 First scientific paper published, *Beschreibung einer neuen Species aus dem Genus Cyprinus Linn., Isis,* X., a presentation by Lorenz Oken, Agassiz's teacher, of Agassiz's discovery of a new species of carp.

1829 First book: a description and cataloguing of Brazilian fishes gathered by the Spix-Von Martius Expedition of 1817-1820. *Selecta genera et species Piscium, quos in itinere per Brasiliam* . . . Published in Munich and presented as a surprise to his parents.
      Received Doctorate of Philosophy.

1830 Received Doctorate of Medicine.

1831 Paris, research at the Jardins des Plantes. Met Baron Cuvier and Alexander von Humboldt, both of whom recognized his genius and encouraged him.

1832 Undertook the study of fossil fishes, declined an offer to teach at Heidelberg, and became professor of Natural History at the newly founded College of Neuchâtel.

1833 Began publication of the study of fossil fishes, *Recherches sur les Poissons fossiles,* a monumental work that would take ten years to complete, the final volume being issued in 1843.
      Married Cecile Braun, sister of his colleague Alexander Braun.

1836 Geological research begun.

1840 Discovery that there have been Ice Ages.
      Études sur les glaciers.

1841 German version of the study of glaciers, *Untersuchungen über die Gletscher.*

1843   Final volume of the *Fossil Fishes*.

1845   Final volume of the study of fresh-water fishes, *Histoire naturelle des poissons d'eau douce de l'Europe centrale*, 1839-1845.

      Iconographie des Coquilles tertiares, a study of fossil shells.

      Monographie des poissons fossiles du vieux grès rouge; ou, Système dévonien (Old Red Sandstone) des îles Britanniques et de Russie.

1846   *Nomenclator zoologicus*, 1842-1846, an index to Zoology. Arrived in America to lecture at the Lowell Institute.

1847   *Nouvelles études et experiences sur les glaciers actuels, leur structure, leur progression et leur action physique sur le sol.*

1848   First course of lectures at Harvard, for the Lawrence Scientific School.

      Principles of Zoology.

      Wife died at Carlsruhe.

1849   *Twelve Lectures on Comparative Embryology.*

1850   Married Elizabeth Cabot Cary.

      Lake Superior: Its Physical Character, Vegetation, and Animals. Studied the Florida reefs.

1854   *Bibliographia zoologicae et geologiae*, a general catalogue of all books, tracts, and memoirs on zoology and geology, 1848-1854.

1855   *Outlines of Comparative Physiology.*

      Agassiz School for Young Ladies, the germ of Radcliffe College. Prospectus for the *Contributions to the Natural History of the United States.*

1857   May 28, his fiftieth birthday, and publication of Vol. I of the *Contributions to the Natural History of The United States*, Vol. II being published later in the year.

1859   Founding of the Museum of Comparative Zoology at Harvard.

1860   Vol. III of the *Contributions*.

1861   Became citizen of the U.S.

1862   Vol. IV of the *Contributions*, the last to be completed.

1863   *Methods of Study in Natural History.*

1865   Expedition to Brazil, lasting until 1866.

1866   *Geological Sketches*, First Series. (Second Series published 1876, edited by Elizabeth Cary Agassiz.)

      The Structure of Animal Life.

1868   Visiting Professor at Cornell, the plan of non-resident professors being his own suggestion.

      A Journey in Brazil, with his wife as co-author.

1869   Stroke.
1871   On board the *Hassler* for an oceanographic voyage (the line
       of study followed by his son Alexander, later director of the
       museum).
1873   Founding of the summer school on Penikese Island.
       Death, December 14, at Cambridge. His name and the word
       "Teacher" are inscribed on an unshaped boulder from the
       glacier of the Aar.
1874   "Evolution and Permanence of Type," *Atlantic Monthly*, Janu-
       ary, 1874.

Bibliographical Note

The text of the "Essay on Classification" is that of the only edition of Agassiz's *Contributions to the Natural History of the United States of America*, Vol. I, Little, Brown and Co., Boston, 1857. The *Contributions* eventually ran to four folio volumes, the fourth appearing in 1862. Volumes II-IV are copiously and handsomely illustrated with lithographs of turtles and jellyfish, many in color; the illustrations in this book have been reproduced from these. Mr. Edward Lurie, Agassiz's most recent biographer, has prepared, since this book was compiled, a critical edition of the "Essay on Classification" for the Harvard University Press, its only complete reprinting since 1857.

"The Physical History of the Amazons" and "Voyage up the Coast to Pará" are taken from *A Journey in Brazil* by Louis and Elizabeth Cary Agassiz (the title page has "by Professor and Mrs. Louis Agassiz"), Ticknor and Fields, Boston, 1867. The text is derived from "a common diary," though the narrative is clearly by Mrs. Agassiz and the scientific observations by the professor. This book was enormously successful and went through six editions in two years.

"Cyanea Arctica" is taken from Vol. IV and "Character" from Vol. II of the *Contributions*. "The Ripening of Leaves" and "Rocks like Flocks of Sheep" come from *Geological Sketches*, Second Series, James R. Osgood and Co., Boston, 1876. This posthumous collection of studies was edited by Mrs. Agassiz and is a second volume to the *Geological Sketches*, Ticknor and Fields, Boston, 1866, from which "The Laurentian Hills" is reprinted. "On the Americans" is from a letter to Milne Edwards in Elizabeth Cary Agassiz's *Louis Agassiz: His Life and Correspondence*, Houghton, Mifflin, and Co., Boston, 1885.

"Nomenclature and Classification" and "Categories of Classification," originally public lectures, are reprinted from *Methods of Study in Natural History*, Ticknor and Fields, Boston, 1863.

"Evolution and Permanence of Type," Agassiz's last essay, appeared in *The Atlantic Monthly*, Vol. XXXIII, 1874.